The Eternity Dialogues

UNDERSTANDING GLOBAL TRANSFORMATION

The Eternity Dialogues

UNDERSTANDING GLOBAL TRANSFORMATION

First Edition

David Derezotes

University of Utah

SAN DIEGO

Bassim Hamadeh, CEO and Publisher

Laura Pasquale, Specialist Acquisitions Editor

Amy Smith, Project Editor

Casey Hands, Associate Production Editor

Jess Estrella, Senior Graphic Designer

Stephanie Kohl, Licensing Coordinator

Natalie Piccotti, Director of Marketing

Kassie Graves, Vice President of Editorial

Jamie Giganti, Director of Academic Publishing

Cover image: Copyright © 2016 iStockphoto LP/Bartosz Hadyniak.

Printed in the United States of America.

cognella® | ACADEMIC PUBLISHING

3970 Sorrento Valley Blvd., Ste. 500, San Diego, CA 92121

Image Credits

Fig. 23.1: Source: https://pixabay.com/photos/apocalypse-war-armageddon-2570868/.

Fig. 24.1: Source: https://pixabay.com/illustrations/drought-desert-elephant-dry-1733889/.

Fig. 25.1: Source: https://pixabay.com/photos/earth-globe-moon-world-planet-1365995/.

Fig. 26.1: Copyright © 2012 Depositphotos/nasirkhan.

Fig. 27.1: Copyright © 2012 Depositphotos/everett225.

Fig. 28.1: Copyright © 2015 Depositphotos/Route55.

Fig. 29.1: Copyright © 2013 Depositphotos/Kwest.

Fig. 30.1: Copyright © 2018 Depositphotos/denisismagilov.

Fig. 31.1: Copyright © 2016 Depositphotos/scusi0-9.

Fig. 32.1: Copyright © 2015 Depositphotos/Rawpixel.

Fig. 33.1: Copyright © 2018 Depositphotos/Nuttawutnuy.

I dedicate this work to my partner, Tami, who has enthusiastically supported this project, and who is a strong woman and gifted healer who inspires and serves others, like the Great-Grandmothers in the Novel. I love you.

Contents

Preface

"My students don't want to read anymore!"

Is It True?

In this era of rapid change, the way we communicate is also changing rapidly. We do know that most students do not complete assigned readings, and other forms of communication are in decline, such as newspaper use, leisure reading, and even television time. However, other forms have increased; videos and CDs contribute to increased library use, cell phones are ubiquitous, and a forest of electronic devices cover most classroom desks.

What Is Going On?

Perhaps our ability to communicate has outpaced our ability to communicate wisely. The only cause of anything is always everything, and the "failure" of our students to read their assignments may best be viewed as a symptom of deeper factors that are both local and global.

We are no doubt living in another historic "communication revolution" with both the opportunities and disappointments that accompany such revolutions. At the same time that technology provides more opportunities for connection, we ironically seem even more disconnected from other people, other living things, our life-supportive ecosystems, and our home universe. In addition, many of us are disappointed with our failures to use this technology for the highest good. Perhaps our rapid technological advancements in communications serve to more intensely remind us of our relative lack of progress in developing the emotional, social, and spiritual "technologies" of consciousness, compassion, and loving kindness that are necessary for our well-being.

In this context, the textbook you have selected offers a different approach.

The Eternity Dialogues is a historical social science novel based on a probable history of humanity's future. It is a future when the technologies of life and death have reached a critical point or "convergence" in which the existence of humanity is endangered by such global survival threats as ecological collapse, widespread despondency, and nuclear war.

It is a convergence of technological advancement in which scientists have developed by 2050 a method of extending life indefinitely, a new way to connect all human beings together through a "mental web" and increasingly lethal and autonomous weapons of mass destruction.

It is also an opportunity for transformation. We meet a group of very old women, the "Great-Grandmothers" who have been preparing secretly for thousands of years to help humanity during this "Convergence." There is a young social worker who has the courage to confront her employers when her first patients who receive the "immortality treatments" become suicidal. There is a young man who has the courage to stand up to his revolutionary brothers when they acquire and want to use weapons of mass destruction. And, finally, Earth is visited by the "SkyWoman," who comes down from the sky to "land" at New Delhi, India, with a message of transformation for humanity. The SkyWoman's approach involves the development of consciousness through an ongoing, "eternal" process of individual self-reflection, guided imagery (that she calls "psychedrama") and global dialogue. She shows the world three different futures that humanity can choose: either destruction, survival, or transformation.

In the story, we meet groups of people who at first are seeking such ego-based goals as power, revenge, or wealth, including CEOs who control the largest corporations, politicians who run the wealthiest countries, religious leaders who direct the most extensive faith communities, and revolutionaries who command the largest terror networks. The groups they lead are all toxic and hierarchical work environments, where minoritized people are silenced. Eventually, each group of people makes transformations, in part because of courageous interventions from those with relatively little power and because of the words and actions of the Great-Grandmothers and the SkyWoman.

I wrote this book because I want humanity to not only *survive* the global survival threats that menace us but also to cocreate an ongoing individual and collective *transformation* in which we reach our potential and foster our highest individual and collective good.

I also believe that such transformation is possible and that the obstacles to our transformation are largely internal. These obstacles can be called "ego."

The Eternity Dialogues challenges students to develop the consciousness necessary to heal our ego. Ego is defined as the individual and collective identification with beliefs that make disconnection, self-hatred, and violence possible. In the story, as key individuals develop consciousness, or "reverent awareness," they begin to heal the ego and feel, think, and act differently.

The book offers students *practical tools* for individual and collective transformation. As future leaders, our students need to know what consciousness (or "mindfulness") is, what dialogue is, and how they are interrelated. They will learn how to develop consciousness through such techniques as individual meditation and guided imagery. Students will also learn what dialogue is, why dialogue is necessary for deep cooperation, and how to facilitate intergroup dialogue between people who may look, think, and behave very differently.

The Eternity Dialogues is actually two volumes that are designed to interconnect with and complement each other:

The *novel* is available in a book form that is written to both entertain and challenge the reader. There are 33 chapters, divided into four sections.

The *learning site* is a web-based companion to the story that has the more traditional elements of a textbook, including chapter summaries, learning objectives, questions for reflection and dialogue, learning scenarios, and annotated bibliographies for each chapter.

Suggestions for How to Use the Text in the Classroom or in Lesson Planning

1. *Multidisciplinary use.* The text is designed to support learning in a number of different fields. I am a professor in both the humanities (peace and conflict studies) and social work (generalist practice, mental health practice, inclusive dialogue, spirituality in social work). The text can also support classes in such related fields as political science, psychology, religious studies, environmental humanities, and business.

2. *The novel and learning site are designed to be complementary.* The text is designed so that instructors can assign the same chapters in the novel each week that you assign in the learning site. Each learning site chapter has web-based tools that can help the student acquire knowledge, skills, and values related to the same chapter in the novel. Students can work independently outside of class on some of the web-based material, and the instructor can also bring some of the web-based questions into the classroom as shared learning activities. The materials are designed so that each instructor has the flexibility to decide how to use them each week, to fit her or his own unique teaching style.

    In the first week of class, for example, the instructor might ask students to read Chapters 1 and 2 in the novel and also complete half of the assignments in Chapters 1 and 2 in the learning site before class. Then the other half of the learning site activities might be used as in-class activities. For a 15-week semester, the instructor will assign two or three chapters each week (some chapters are longer than others).

3. *Single lecture approaches.* If the instructor wants to use part of the text for a single lecture, the same approach described earlier can be used. She might begin the class with an opportunity for general questions and comments and then ask students to identify the theoretical concepts. Students can discover these concepts by keeping in mind the "key themes" described at the beginning of each chapter in the novel, as well as by reviewing the learning objectives described in each chapter in the learning site. The instructor can also use some of the learning site questions for in-class activities.

4. *Learning by doing.* Instructors are encouraged to use most of the classroom time in interactive and experiential learning activities, because adults generally learn best through such active approaches and because the novel and learning site are written to stimulate self-reflection, curiosity about the world, critical thinking, and critical feeling.

5. *Annotated bibliography.* The annotated bibliography in each learning site chapter can be used by students to do further independent exploration of a key theme identified in the novel or learning site. For a final assignment, the instructor can ask students to do in-depth independent research on a topic from one of the chapters, and the annotated bibliography can also help the students get started on doing a literature review for such a research project.

I welcome your comments and questions. Thank you for using **The Eternity Dialogues** in your classroom.

David Derezotes
University of Utah, Salt Lake City
January 2019

Acknowledgments

I WANT TO ACKNOWLEDGE the staff at Cognella who have all been kind and supportive from the very beginning of this project. Thanks especially to Laura Pasquale, who was open from the beginning to my idea of using a novel as a teaching tool and who patiently guided me through the first year.

Thank you to my friends and colleagues and students who listened to my ideas and encouraged me, sometimes as we sat at the table by the coffeehouse window, drinking coffee and watching the Sugarhouse traffic go by; sometimes at the main desk of the College, trading stories and laughing; and sometimes on our dialogue radio program, finding the "Radical Middle" on KRCL.

Thank you also to the authors and artists who most inspired me over the years; including J. Krishnamurti, Isaac Asimov, Eckhart Tolle, Pema Chödrön, Robert Alex Johnson, and Stevie Wonder.

Finally, gratitude to the Great Mystery that inspires all of us, and to those dark clear New Moon desert nights when Sky's Spine rotates slowly across the summer sky.

Author's Note

ALTHOUGH THE NOVEL and accompanying learning site are based on the author's science-based speculation of future events, the novel is a fictitious story, and any resemblance to actual people or events are purely accidental.

SECTION I

Convergence

CHAPTER 1

The Great-Grandmothers

Key themes in scene:
1. The Great-Grandmothers
2. The Mother-of-Us-All
3. The Dream

Location: Loiyangalani on Lake Turkana, Great Rift Valley, Kenya
Date: June 20, 2050

For more than 100,000 years, they had returned to meet for council at the solstice time. This meeting was different.

They all knew it could be their last gathering.

The women sit in circle. Although familiar, they've not gathered for a year, and there's much catching up to do.

The evening wind off Lake Turkana nudges the few palms planted by the house, bringing a welcome coolness as the sun drops red over the Great Rift Valley. They smell fresh Nile perch cooking in traditional Kenyan niter kibbeh, with injera and shiro simmering in the pans.

One of the women stands slowly. Quite small in stature, her skin is very dark and wrinkled, and her long white hair braided and beaded down her back. Her eyes are small, but warm and intense, as if a soft light is shining through them from inside her.

Everyone is suddenly quiet, not out of fear but respect for the one they call Mother-of-Us-All. She starts to speak:

"Welcome, thank you all for coming to Loiyangalani on our Jade Sea. I know many of you have traveled far. I too have traveled far. I am Barannda Estava Maronna, my great-grandmother was Misorri Estava Maronna. We lived here on these shores almost two hundred thousand years ago." Her eyes look way beyond the little yard where they sit.

"When I was a child, my sisters and I ran along the lake, chasing the marabouts back into the air and waiting for my mother to cook the fish. The sky and water were clean then and full of life.

"You call me Mother-of-Us-All. Yes, I was the first to look like a modern human, but there were many who came before me. Today, our children are taught that humanity began with the race they call *Homo sapiens*, but our humanity came from our ancestors, well before the time of our current race ... and I knew them.

"Yes, they did not look so much like us today, but they laughed and lived and loved and died just like us. Their language tools and trade were not like ours, but they left their bones in the dust around this lake ... their time is gone now." The wind pushes a tear across her cheek, as she continues. "As you all know, we are now living in the days of the *Convergence*. People who look like us have lived on this Earth only a few hundred thousand years and already have built machines that can kill us all—machines that postpone death and now machines that talk with our thoughts."

She gestures her hands up in the air. "But no machines for making sense!"

The women laugh.

Barannda Estava Maronna stops and looks at the circle of faces, all in silence now. *The Great-Grandmothers* all sit comfortably on the floor. They bring a diversity of skin colors, body shapes, and clothing. They all wear tiny wooden figures, hung from their neck, of female elephants.

"We are the Great-Grandmothers, the Elephant clan. We wear wooden figures of the matriarch of the elephants, who leads the herd in their migrations, finding the ancient routes, finding sources of water and food.

"We have all lived many lives together, and we have all chosen to stay, coming back again and again to serve as matriarchs to help our people. Now they need our help more than ever. We have anticipated these events and have made our plans."

Now, Aaradhya, you wish to speak?

One of the Great-Grandmothers rises to speak. "Thank you, everyone. I am Aaradhya Sargretti, my great-grandmother was Kashvri Sargretti. I had a dream before I left for Africa, which I will share with you today.

"I am walking at home, in the morning, at Raj Ghat in New Delhi, which is our memorial to Mahatma Gandhi. A great stairway appears in the sky overhead, descending to a spot at my feet. An endless crowd of people assembles around me, praying and chanting. I look up to see a figure walking down slowly toward me. When she steps upon Earth and removes her scarf, I only then recognize her as me."

Barannda smiles and walks over to touch the woman's face. "I have had the same dream, my sister. As have we all."

Everyone nods.

"As I said, we have anticipated these events and have made our plans. It is time now to put our plans into action."

"We have called for help. Soon Earth will have a visitor."

CHAPTER 2

The Social Worker

Key themes in scene:
1. The immortality treatments
2. The psychological challenges of immortality
3. The challenges and opportunities of social
work in a corporate environment

Location: Downtown San Francisco, California
Date: June 20, 2050

"Mr. Hauser killed himself last night."

The words repeat over and over. Will this mean the end of her job? And, more importantly, will all her patients eventually kill themselves?

Deanna Bradley's thoughts dominate her consciousness as she stares out the window at the Golden Gate Bridge, its red scaffolding half hidden in the morning fog. She can still hear her supervisor's voice from an hour ago, telling her that her first client was dead.

Not that it was totally unexpected. Mr. Hauser had become increasingly depressed and suicidal since he began the immortality treatments about six months ago. She thought she had done all the right things—followed the protocol. She had asked him if he would be willing to call someone before he killed himself. They had discussed support systems, and she noted the conversations in her case notes. She told herself that it was not her fault, yet she still felt somehow responsible.

Now she watches as the big table fills with people for the weekly case staffing.

Still in her mid-20s, Deanna had been pleased when she was hired as a medical social worker for Greater Bay Area Biotech in downtown San Francisco. It wasn't easy to get a job right out of the master's in social work program. She had known then that she wanted to work with people who were struggling with physical health, but she had never anticipated working with wealthy and privileged clients. And she had been surprised that they had picked a young woman like herself for the job.

When she was told that the firm was offering the first immortality treatments, Deanna had been surprised again. She had read that scientists were working on the treatments, but she had not heard that they were ready to offer them to people. When the firm did their first public announcement, she was told to keep quiet about her own work at the clinic. It was then that she started to wonder if they had hired her *because* she was so young, looked even younger than she was, and, perhaps, thought she would be easy to manipulate. She knew otherwise. No one had ever been able to control Deanna Bradley!

Randy Snyder, the clinic manager, stands and walks over to close the door. He wears a gray business suit, and his hair and beard are groomed perfectly.

"Well, let's start the meeting. I think we all know by now that our first patient, Mr. Hauser, committed suicide last night with a handgun in his condo. Why a man as financially successful as Mr. Hauser would kill himself after spending almost two million dollars on a treatment for immortality escapes me. Was it some kind of mental illness? Dr. Yin?"

Dr. Yin is the clinic medical director. On the original genetics study team in Shanghai, he was the first physician to bring the immortality treatments to the United States. Short, ambitious, and overweight, Dr. Yin has a nervous energy that he seems to bring with him wherever he goes. Today, he is particularly upset.

"We really don't understand yet why Mr. Hauser had these symptoms. The original trials with chimpanzees in China were completely successful. Dr. Walker?"

Dr. Delores Walker is the staff psychiatrist. She is tall and thin, with short brown hair and a formal demeanor.

"Yes, thank you. Actually, a few of our patients are experiencing symptoms of depression and anxiety. We have consulted with our colleagues in China and Brazil, and they are seeing similar symptoms in some of their patients. Our colleagues in Shanghai have had some success with the administration of a cocktail of some of the latest antidepressant and antianxiety gen meds."

Randy Snyder looks down at his notes. "That is great news, Delores. Can we get this cocktail here as soon as possible?"

Dr. Walker nods.

"Well," Randy continues, "I hope you all understand how important it is that we keep this information confidential. I was not aware that other patients were having ... uh ... difficulties, but I am confident we will find the correct medications. I am proud to let you all know that this clinic has already exceeded the expectations of our parent corporation by one hundred and seventy-five percent. We are looking at a new batch of referrals coming in next week. With these kinds of profits, the parent corporation is already looking to expand our services into other locations in the Los Angeles area. When we submit our six-month financial statement, you all stand to get a significant bonus."

Everyone in the room claps, except Deanna.

Deanna looks up from her note pad. "May I say something?" She had become used to being ignored in these meetings. She wondered if it was because of her gender or her age or both.

Randy rolls his eyes impatiently. "Well, go ahead, Miss Bradley."

"As your social worker, I have a responsibility to this clinic to work hard and be a team player. But I also have a responsibility to my patients. I learned that in my social work program. Mr. Hauser was a wonderful man. I had gotten to know him quite well, and he told me ... things about himself that made me realize that these treatments we are giving people may have some unanticipated side effects."

"What kinds of things?" asks Dr. Walker.

"Well, he said that he was having dreams ... or actually the same dream, over and over again. He said he kept dreaming that he was running away from something, in a kind of terror, but that whenever he turned around to see what was chasing him, it was himself!"

"There is no scientific evidence that dreams are anything but a side effect of the brain replenishing itself every evening!"

"That may be, Dr. Walker, but there is one more thing."

"Yes?"

"Mr. Hauser asked me if it would be possible to reverse the treatment and become mortal again."

"Why would he do that?" asked Dr. Walker.

"I am not sure. When I told him that to my understanding, the treatments are irreversible, he said, 'I was so afraid of death, and now that it is gone, I have realized I am even more scared of life.' I still wonder what he meant."

CHAPTER 3

The Chief Executive Officers

Key themes in scene:
1. The wealth and power of corporations
2. The values and insecurities corporate leaders can have

Location: Buenos Aires, Argentina, Puerto Madero district
Date: June 20, 2050

The men sitting at the table rule the world.

And none of them are yet aware of how they are each ruled in turn by something in their own minds.

Overlooking the busy port of Buenos Aries, the executive suite of Global Multinationals Unlimited (GMU) is expansive and well equipped with meeting rooms, a bar, and a sauna.

The men relax around the table as they wait for the president of GMU to join them. Mr. Cheng arrives at the door at precisely 1:00 p.m. The men clap as Mr. Cheng takes a seat at the head of the great table.

He nods politely and begins speaking.

"At this table are seated the CEOs of the eleven biggest multinational corporations in the world. Collectively, we control about sixty percent of global wealth. Last year, our share of global earnings was sixty-eight percent. Next year, we expect sales of our new war robots and immortality treatments to increase earnings by seventeen percent. Can we have a report on our robots, Mr. Mikhailov?"

Mr. Mikhailov initiates a 3-D display in the center of the table. An image of a robot appears, rotating slowly in the air.

"This is the ninety-four hundred series war robot. This model is capable of running at thirty-five kilometers an hour and can leap over obstacles ten meters high and fifteen meters wide. It can be equipped with jet propulsion and has deep-water capabilities. It is equipped with close- and long-range laser weapons. It has all-weather, day/night sensor capabilities. We already have orders from Russia, India, Japan, and Mexico, with thirteen other countries expressing interest. The ninety-four hundred represents such a leap in destructive power that no nation can do without it!"

"Very good, Mr. Mikhailov," Mr. Cheng says. "Mr. Smythe, I understand you are now supervising our public relations efforts."

"Yes, sir. We have been making small donations to cities and universities that we think would improve our public image. We target programs that we can control and ultimately use to generate more income. For example, we now control indirectly or directly over eighty percent of all the genetic research in the world."

"Excellent! Now, speaking of genetics, can we have a report on the immortality treatments? Mr. Hiroki?"

Mr. Hiroki nervously initiates the wall screen and a display of tables appears.

"As you know, our laboratories in Guangzhou spent ten years testing the genetic procedures on chimpanzees. We began our first immortality treatments on humans six months ago in pilot locations in China, Japan, India, Mexico, Brazil, England, Germany, and the USA.

"These eight pilot facilities have sold about one thousand procedures in our first six months of operations, at 1.75 million dollars each, which gave us earnings of 1.75 billion over the first two quarters. Our next generation of immortality centers will be opening up across the world in a few weeks. We estimate that there are about ten million people who are both wealthy and interested enough to purchase immortality treatments over the first decade of our program. We can actually produce the genetic treatments for about one hundred dollars per person, which gives us a profit margin of seventeen thousand five hundred percent. This means the immortality project will overtake our military projects in profitability in a few years."

Mr. Hiroki looks over at Mikhailov and smiles. Mikhailov scowls back at him.

"There is one ... small complication we are seeing in some of the clinics."

"Yes?" Mr. Cheng says.

"Some of the patients seem to become depressed after they get the treatments. Actually, the first human who received the immortality treatment six months ago died last night, by his own hands."

"You mean he killed himself?"

"Um ... yes. However, our psychiatry section is already testing a cocktail of medications to give to patients who have similar reactions. We think that the demand for the cocktail will increase as we sell more immortality treatments, which will ultimately increase profits. And our lawyers have already changed our intake forms to eliminate any future legal risk. Our lobbyists are working with our political friends to create new policies that require patients who have emotional difficulties to submit to binding arbitration if they wish to bring suit."

"Well done, Mr. Hiroki! And Mr. Brocktone? You were assigned to take control of this other new discovery in communications. I believe it is by scientists in France and Korea?"

Mr. Brocktone clears his throat. He is a tall Englishman in a tan colored suit.

"Actually, the Koreans took the lead on this project. From what we understand, the scientists have created the technology necessary for a new kind of Mental Network, as they call it, in which one only has to think in order to communicate with other people. Simultaneous translation provides the possibility of people all over the world instantly communicating with each other. They are ready to test this technology over great distances. Obviously, this project could lead to incredible financial opportunity for Global Multinationals, perhaps with the *biggest* profit potential to date."

He looks at Mr. Mikhailov and Mr. Hiroki, and they *both* scowl back at him.

"And have you secured a financial interest in this project for us?" Mr. Cheng asks.

"Not yet. So far, they have resisted accepting any corporate investments, but I am not worried. We are arranging a meeting with their lead scientist."

Mr. Smythe interrupts eagerly. "Perhaps an offer to construct a new building for each campus might be persuasive, or a new football stadium if necessary. As they say, every institution has a price."

"Very good then, Mr. Smythe. You will join Mr. Brocktone in this meeting with the scientist. We expect to hear some good news from both of you soon."

CHAPTER 4

The Politicians

Key themes in scene:
1. The power of wealthy nations
2. The values and insecurities politicians can have

Location: Al Fanateer Beach in Al Jubail, Saudi Arabia
Date: June 20, 2050

They had all learned to present a public smile, even when they were suffering.

And today, they all suffered from the knowledge that the survival of humanity was in their hands.

The leaders of the "Group of Thirteen" pose for their annual photo shoot in front of the Persian Gulf, with a sea of reporters watching.

They represent the 13 most powerful economies of 2015, including China, India, the United States, Indonesia, Brazil, The Unified Republic of Korea, Russia, the United Kingdom, Mexico, Japan, Turkey, Germany, and Saudi Arabia. This year, they are enjoying a stay at the best resort on Al Fanateer Beach in Al Jubail, Saudi Arabia.

They are directed to the dinner prepared by their Saudi hosts. The food and atmosphere are elaborate, and they are surrounded by waitresses and waiters.

Soon the doors are closed, and the 13 leaders sit alone with their desserts. The current president of the Group of Thirteen is Mr. Kusumo from Indonesia. He stands up and welcomes everyone.

"I want to thank our Saudi hosts for this wonderful meal! Your city here is beautiful! Now it is time for us to begin our conversations. We have several pressing topics. First, we are all concerned about this growing civil war in Southern Syria. Second, there has been a new wave of terror threats, and they all seemed linked to this new international organization called Global One. Third, we have been unable to agree on a plan to control the proliferation of these new robots of war. Fourth, the 2045 trade agreements need to be adjusted to reflect the remarkable economic growth trends in Africa and the Middle East. Finally, we are all concerned about the growing unrest in a number of countries regarding the new immortality treatments. Any comments?"

Mr. Schmidt from Germany stands up. "I just received word that street violence has been reported in Berlin and Hamburg, following protests about the cost of these immortality treatments."

President Emily Browning from the United States, one of the two women in the group, joins in. "We have word that similar protests are happening in some of our cities as well. We can't really blame people for being upset that these treatments cost almost two million dollars, and besides—"

"We can't allow these protests to get out of hand, Emily," interrupts President Çelik from Turkey in his loud scolding voice. "Can't Global Multinationals offer the middle class some kind of reduced cost treatments? Maybe just extend their lives a few more years at a bargain price?" he says with a laugh.

President Browning looks President Çelik in the eye and responds, "Even when a brown woman is president of the second-most powerful nation in the world, she is still interrupted, and talked down to, by *some* men."

The room is uncomfortably silent for a moment as President Çelik sighs and shrugs his shoulders dramatically.

"Can we go back to the terror threat?" asks Premier Petrov from Russia. "We have information that there has been an unusual level of conversation in Crimea concerning interest in the purchase of some of the new killer robots. We have reason to believe that terrorist elements have either purchased or are in the process of purchasing these weapons."

"For what purpose?" asks Mr. Kusumo.

"Our intelligence services believe that the international terrorist elements—they call themselves New Beginnings—are going to make a demonstration and present a list of demands to the Group of Thirteen. In fact, we are expecting an announcement at any moment."

"What kind of demonstration?"

"A major mass casualty attack on one or more of our great cities," Premier Petrov says. "And one more thing. We believe that elements associated with Global Multinationals may be directly involved in these sales."

CHAPTER 5

The Clerics

Key themes in scene:
1. Power of religious leaders
2. The values and insecurities religious leaders can have

Location: Todaiji in Nara, Japan:
Date: June 20, 2050

He did not like to think of himself as ambitious.

But he liked being the leader of one of the most powerful churches on the planet. Now he would soon stand in front of the entire World Summit as their elected leader.

A gathering of people sit politely in the auditorium as the speaker rises, the Honorable Pope Luca. A display of giant screens behind the speaker show live feeds of other audiences watching the event at sites across the globe. The simulacrum of the pope is in the air above each audience, projected by the TeleTouch units.

"Welcome to the 2050 World Summit of Religious Leaders! Welcome to those of you sitting here with us in this beautiful garden in Nara, Japan, as well as to all of you participating around the world through this global interactive broadcast. Through our latest translation devices, we will all be able to participate in these sessions in their own languages!

"Tonight, we will begin our summit with an evening of sacred music from different traditions. But first, I will be delivering a brief message of peace as we are in the Easter season—one of the most sacred times in my own tradition—"

The pope is interrupted by a voice that seems to emanate from the central screen.

"Excuse me, Pope Luca. I am sorry to interrupt, but I feel that I must protest. I am calling from the new nation of Southern Syria, which, as you all know, is now torn by a terrible civil war. Even now, my people are being killed by the robots that are apparently being tested here by your corporations! There is no peace in my land, only unending violence. Right now, we don't need music and celebration; we need action. We need a cease-fire; we need food and shelter and medicine. What can your summit do to address this injustice?"

The pope whispers to his aide, "Who is this man, and how is *he* able to gain access to our event?"

A number of other voices are now competing for attention. Images of clerics shouting appear on all the screens.

"How dare you interrupt the pope!"

"And what will you do about the blasphemy of these immortality treatments?"

"It's about time we talked about what is really going on!"

"Can't we all get along?"

The pope raises his voice. "Shut it down, please. Shut it all down!"

In a moment, all the screens go blank, and the audience is suddenly sitting in silence in the dark of the new moon in Nara.

Quickly recovering and pulling himself together, the pope swallows down his fear and turns to the audience.

"Let us pray."

CHAPTER 6

The Scientists

Key themes in scene:
1. The challenges and opportunities of scientific
work in a corporate era
2. The values and insecurities scientists can have

Location: Incheon National University Incheon, Korea
Date: June 20, 2050

They are ready to make history.

Dr. Jiu Kang sits with her science team, the Communication Technology Lab, at Incheon National University in Korea. They all repeat their own passwords in their minds and at the same time make the hand motions to open up the program.

Their sensors show that their mental energies are being picked up by microsatellites orbiting above them and information is being transmitted around the planet.

In the air above them are the simulacrums of their colleagues Dr. Adele Dubois and her team at the University of Lorraine in Nancy, France. Dr. Dubois and her team are also thinking their passwords and making the hand motions.

Dr. Kang nods as she thinks the password of her colleague Dr. Adele Dubois in France.

Suddenly, there are smiles on the faces of Dr. Kang and Dr. Dubois as they connect their thoughts together. Each of the other people in Korea and France also "dials in" to the little network.

Dr. Kang stands up.

"My colleagues, congratulations!" she thinks, "We have just made history. Human beings are now capable of communicating with each other across the planet, directly through our thoughts! And our language translation technology is operating effectively through the microsatellites as I speak! We have just activated the World Wide Mental Web!

"As you know, as the first wave of networked intercommunication evolved into the second wave or World Wide Web, communication technologies became increasingly centralized in the hands of large corporations and the governments they controlled. Public concerns about privacy, confidentiality, hacking, and political propaganda were largely ignored by this powerful corporate elite. As a third wave the Internet of Everything gradually linked humanity and all of our technologies together, attempts to decentralize the architecture of the web were defeated by the elite.

"However, our Mental Web uses the natural energy of the human mind and the unique human DNA code to transmit thoughts and images. Our Mental Web enables people to take back control of their communication technology. We can avoid the existing web architecture completely and communicate directly with each other through our own minds. The satellites are the only technology required, so we can offer this ability to communicate to everyone on the planet, regardless of where they live or who they are.

"We want to acknowledge the work of our colleagues in our sister institution in France, as well as the collaboration of other colleagues across the world who have helped develop components of this new system."

There are a number of congratulatory thoughts in agreement.

Dr. Kang continues to think. "I am especially proud that we have developed this technology over the past decade using only private grants. This means that the technology is now available to every person on the planet, and no corporation or government will be able to control implementation, distribution, or prices.

"We have already worked out an agreement with our colleagues in Salt Lake City to launch the additional microsatellites necessary to connect everyone on Earth to the Mental Web. This will be accomplished in a few days, as the satellites are being readied at our launching facilities in the Great Salt Lake Desert. There will, of course, still be technical challenges to overcome and techniques to refine, but the groundwork has been established!"

"Yes," thinks Dr. Dubois. "It is time for us to break open the finest French champagne and Korean makgeolli, which we have provided for this occasion!"

Dr. Kang is not smiling, however. She thinks to everyone, softly but earnestly, "My colleagues, I fear that humanity may not be ready for this new technology. I am concerned that there are probably people right now plotting to use our new technology for their own purposes in the service of their own agenda, power, or greed."

The reality is that the threat is even worse than Dr. Kang imagines.

CHAPTER 7

The Revolutionaries

Key themes in scene:
1. The values and insecurities revolutionaries can have
2. "Angry-young-man energy"
3. Motivations for violence

Location: Washington, DC
Date: June 20, 2050

They are warriors, and soon they will have control of weapons that could lead to humanity's destruction. Most of them have what their elders might describe as "angry-young-man energy."

Unfortunately, no elder has yet arisen who could help them temper their new power with the perspective of maturity. If destruction is to be avoided, they will have to do that themselves.

A group of 12 men sit in a darkened room in a neighborhood near Howard University. They are of mixed racial and ethnic origins. They represent nine countries and six continents. All are in their 20s or early 30s. They all wear masks as a precaution against infiltration by the police.

One of the men speaks. "As you all know, we rarely meet together in person like this, but our communications are under increasingly effective surveillance. That is why we decided to call as many of our lieutenants together as we could. We thought that they would not suspect us meeting here in Washington. Everyone is here, right?"

"Yes, let's begin our meeting!"

"Billy?"

"Our cell in Crimea has made contact with an agent who will sell us the bombs and robots. They will make the delivery in Istanbul. We will take the weapons by ship to ports in Indonesia and the United States."

"Wait! I thought we agreed that we would not harm any innocent people. All we need to do is explode the bomb somewhere away from people."

"That has not been decided yet."

"How can we possibly promote peace by murdering millions of people?"

"We must do something. The corporations now control our lives and our deaths. They have turned almost every major country into a fascist state. They have most of the world's wealth and military power, and if we wait much longer, they will use their robots to solidify their global domination. And now they have found a way to live forever—a method none of us can afford!"

One young man takes off his mask. Jean-Paul is about 30 years old, with dark-brown skin and eyes.

"You all know me. I understand all these things, my brothers. You all know I am from Colombia. As a boy, I saw people in my village murdered by the soldiers. I saw my own family taken away, never to return. But I also understand that we cannot bring deep peace and justice to a world through war and violence. It has never worked in history. Why would it work now?"

Another young man pulls off his mask. Dmytro is tall with blue eyes and long dark hair. "And you all know me as well! I also know violence in my homeland of Ukraine! My ancestors have been murdered by both Europeans and Asians. And now our cities are all dirty from the factories and our farms are owned by multinational corporations. My people are dying, not from overt war, but from corporate greed that has infected our planet. I say we strike at one of their cities! Violence is all they understand!"

The room is silent. Then Jean-Paul responds.

"Give me a month. I will contact the corporate leadership and tell them that we are armed. I will work out an agreement with them, without any more bloodshed."

Dmytro responds, "All right then. But not a month. There is no time to waste. We will announce to the world that we have the bomb now. We will give you one week to work your peaceful solution."

CHAPTER 8

The Ordinary Family

Key themes in scene:
1. The values and insecurities of this middle-class family in the USA
2. Challenges and opportunities of parenting
children in the 2050 environment

Location: Salt Lake City, Utah
Date: June 20, 2050

A people's history, it could be said, tells the stories of so-called ordinary people, who may live so-called ordinary lives.

Perhaps Phil was an ordinary person who suddenly found himself in extraordinary circumstances.

Looking at his watch and swearing under his breath, Phil Parker finally arrives at his suburban home near the foothills of the Oquirrh Mountains. The drive around I-215 to West Valley used to take only 45 minutes back in 2018 when he started working at the university. That was about the time when he bought his last gas-powered truck.

Phil watches as the car starts to recharge automatically before going inside. Now almost everyone drives electric vehicles; it is difficult to find real gasoline. Phil's vehicle, assembled in Indonesia, is bright yellow, with bumper stickers the kids picked up in California last summer at SpaceLand Park in Los Angeles.

Looking across the valley, he cannot even see the East Bench, where he works at Utah Communications Technology in University Research Park. He shakes his head at the brown color of the sky. With all the clean air technology available now, it seems inexcusable that the local politicians still resist passing clean air legislation.

Phil's partner, Sid, walks out to greet him. "I kept everything warm in the Solarwave. No worries. How was your day, dude?"

Phil smiles a tired smile. "We heard today that our colleagues in Korea and France have successfully tested the system. It looks like the satellites we helped build will be an integral part of the new global Mental Web. We got the go-ahead to launch the satellite vehicles from the Great Salt Lake in a day or two."

"Wow, that's great."

"Yes and no. That means we will all be doing a lot of overtime this summer."

Knowing how Phil can get stressed, Sid gives him a kiss on the cheek and then a stress pill. As they walk in, he yells, "Matti! Benton! Frederick! Time for dinner now!"

As Matti and Benton sit down for their meal, Sid turns on the TeleTouch above the dinner table. Although it is now almost 7:00 p.m., the 6:00 p.m. news comes on, automatically saved. Sid's son Frederick comes in wearing a gaming mixed-reality helmet. Annoyed, Sid leans over and taps the top of the helmet and scowls. Frederick takes it off.

The announcer speaks. "Today, President Browning is hosting an unexpected press conference." The president's simulacrum appears above them.

"Fellow Americans, by now most of you are probably aware that we are facing several global challenges. News of the new immortality treatments in California has led to protests in many of our larger cities. I do not blame our citizens for their concern that this new medical procedure is so expensive. Our administration is committed to conducting an investigation into why these costs are so high. We also ask our citizens to engage in peaceful protests but please avoid any violent behavior.

"In addition, most of you have heard through social media that the Global One organization has threatened to destroy a city. Our military intelligence is cooperating with our allies to find these terrorists and deal with this threat. We have no reason to believe that any of our citizens are in immediate danger.

"Finally, we have all heard by now the announcements that scientists in Korea and France have developed the technology necessary for what they are calling the Mental Web or what the media has called the Global Mental Network or 'GMN.' The United States is committed to ensuring that all Americans, as well as citizens of other nations, have access to this technology. Our diplomats are at this hour involved in contacting officials in Korea and France."

"That is the program that Phil is a part of, everyone!"

"Just a small part, really. Wow," says Phil, "who would have thought that we would see all these kinds of things coming down at once!"

"Yes, it is weird that it is happening all at the same time," responds Sid.

"Daddy?" asks Matti. "Are they gonna blow up a city? Could they blow up our city?"

Phil looks down at his daughter. She is only eight and already asking tough questions, he thinks. "I hope not dear. It is possible that they might hurt people, but the chances of them hurting us in our city are small. They want to scare us, and we are not going to let them do that."

"Why do they want to scare us?"

"Because they think that if they scare us, we will give them what they want."

"What do they want?"

"I'm not sure, dear. Maybe they want money. Maybe they want more power. Or just more."

"But," asks her brother, "when we were at Mom's house on Sunday, she said that they have war robots that have laser guns on them!"

Sid looks up at Phil and waits for his nod. "Yes, Benton, that is true. There are robots that can do that now."

"Cool! But why do people want to kill other people they don't even know?"

Sid looks up at Phil again. "Benton, you are in fifth grade now. Tell me what you think."

"Hmm ... because they hate them?"

Sid responds, "That might be true, Benton. Remember that hate and anger are different. Everyone has anger, and anger can help motivate us to do good, like when a superhero gets mad and stops the bad guys. Hate is resentment; it is when anger keeps going and becomes a desire for revenge."

CHAPTER 9

Interlude: Racing to Immortality

Key themes in scenes:
1. The sexist and sociopathic traits in one man in a hurry to "win"
2. The challenges of being married to, or working
with, a man like Mr. Hauser

Location: San Francisco, California
Date: January 2050

Billy James Hauser always got what he wanted, whether it was toys, power, women, or wealth. The reason for this was not so much that he was any smarter or more beautiful than most other humans; it was mostly that he would do anything to win.

You can see this in the way he drives or, more accurately, in the way he tells his robot to drive. Despite the overpopulation, San Francisco resisted building more freeways. Yet by midcentury, the freeways and bridges feeding the city were in over-capacity all day and night, all week long. To Billy J., any driving situation, especially on a freeway, is like a chessboard. He is always willing to take chances to cut off other drivers and maneuver around those ponderous electric semis at 160 km an hour with only centimeters to spare.

This all causes conflict with both the robots and people in his life. From the moment they drive off the carport each morning, Billy J. argues with his robot, Chuck, who, of course, was programmed to drive much more cautiously than Billy. And right before he divorced her, his fifth wife Sylvia told Billy J., "Winning is your heroin, babe! You like that buzz, but then you crash, and that boredom comes back again and again."

So maybe it was mostly this addiction to winning that led Billy J. to want to be the first human in the city to get the immortality treatments when he heard about the procedure. And he was.

On his first visit to Greater Bay Area Biotech, he took his then wife Sylvia with him. She liked to sit in the back of their e-convertible because she felt safer. Billy J. and Chuck sat up front.

"_____ it, Chuck! I've told you a million times that I won't waste time waiting in this kind of traffic! Can't you take some side street? My appointment is in ten minutes!"

"Sorry, Mr. Hauser," Chuck replied calmly. "All my data indicates that we are on the fastest route to Greater Bay Area Biotech."

"You call this fast?"

"Darling, would you like a stress pill?" asked Sylvia in her little voice from the back seat.

"I would like you to shut up! That would relieve my stress!"

Sylvia sighed inside but said nothing. Over the two years of their marriage, Billy J. had become increasing verbally abusive as their romance wore off. Sylvia had wondered why she had not seen that side of him when they were dating. But it didn't make her mad once she had found another lover. And she also loved their house, which was right on the water in Sausalito.

The first person Billy J. talked with at Greater Bay Area Biotech was Deanna Bradley. Sitting in her office with Sylvia and Chuck on either side of him, Billy J. had immediately noticed Deanna's appearance. She was probably less than half his age, thin, and athletic.

His first words were in his typical impatient and patriarchal mode. "*You* are my social worker? You must be barely 20. Well, can we get started now, finally?"

Deanna, having read her textbooks in school and attended most of the lectures, however boring they were, noticed that Mr. Hauser had many of the traits of a sociopathic personality, including a desire to "win" at life, a lack of concern for the well-being of the community, and a superficial presentation of charm and intelligence. She remembered her professor saying that many leaders in organizations, institutions, and communities have sociopathic tendencies because they will do anything to succeed in the organization but are also careful to "kiss up to" and please people who have more power than they do.

Deanna smiled and responded calmly. "I'm sorry, Mr. Hauser. I understand that you are anxious to proceed with the immortality treatments. You will be receiving a regimen of genetic treatments every week for the next 90 days. The staff at Biotech designed an intake procedure that begins with a form that we have to complete before you meet with the doctor and receive your first treatment."

"Look, sweetheart, I know that they taught you to say all that kind of thing in graduate school, but come on for God's sake, I am your *first* patient. How can there possibly already be a procedure?" As Deanna smiled back at him with her kind but determined stare, it started to dawn on Billy J. that this young woman would not relent and that he would have to cooperate. "OK fine. Let's go. I haven't got all day."

"So," Deanna began, "your first question. Why do you want to be immortal?"

"Well, doesn't everyone?" Billy J. replied.

"Why no, there are many views on this subject across the world. Social scientists have found that the majority of people are ambivalent about living forever. Actually, it is people who fit your profile who are most likely to want immortality."

"What profile?"

"Men over sixty," Deanna said.

"Hmm. Well, tell me why anyone would *not* want to be immortal?"

"The most common reasons given are that they would miss their loved ones and that they would witness human extinction."

"Well, I'm not worried about any of that!"

Billy J. did not see Sylvia wince at his words.

One Month Later, Deanna Bradley's Office

Billy J. arrives to meet with Deanna for a progress session.

"So how are you doing Mr. Hauser?"

"You can call me Billy J."

"I prefer using Mr. Hauser. So how are you?"

Knowing better than to argue with her, Billy J. looks down at his pluton watch. "Oh, I don't know. Sylvia moved out you know."

"I did not know. I am sorry."

"No worries. It is a big relief really. Hey, I know you are only a social worker, but I wonder if you can get me something. You know, a feel-better pill of some kind."

"Why do you need a feel-better pill if you are so relieved?" Deanna asks. Mr. Hauser is silent, so she adds, "She did *matter* to you. Didn't she?"

More silence.

"Mr. Hauser, I wonder, what do you do with your sadness?"

The uncomfortable silence continues.

"And I am also wondering, how is your mother? Last time, you told me she was in hospice."

"Oh ... well, the hospice doctors say that she may not last another week now. They are giving her meta-opiates so she can't feel the cancer anymore—probably can't feel anything anymore. At least I don't have to listen to her complaints every week now—"

"Does your mother like to complain?"

"That's *all* she likes to do!"

"Is that why you like to complain, Mr. Hauser? Did you learn it from her?"

Another Month Later, Deanna Bradley's Office

"So you decided not to go to the funeral?"

"Right."

"And what did you decide to do with her body?"

"We went with cremation"

"Did you ever hear from your sister?"

"She voice-texted me yesterday from her place in Chicago. She didn't want to go to the funeral either."

"I wonder who *did* attend the funeral? You said your mother never knew for sure who your father was, and you only have one half sister that you knew of. Did your mother have any friends?"

"*Nobody* went to the funeral, OK? Except for the hospice chaplain."

"Sad isn't it?" Deanna says.

"No!"

"Why does it make you angry whenever I ask you about your feelings?"

"I'm *not* angry!"

"Do you think it is bad to be angry?"

Silence

"Well, Mr. Hauser, how *would* you feel if no one attended your funeral?"

"I wouldn't care because I'd be dead, remember? I'd finally have some peace from all this _____."

"But you're not going to *ever* die now, are you?"

Another Month Later, Deanna Bradley's Office

"So what do you think happens when you die, Mr. Hauser?"

"I was going to ask you the same question, Ms. Bradley."

"If you are asking for my personal belief, I will share my own little 't' truth with you. I am a social worker, not a member of the clergy, so I don't have a responsibility to tell people what the capital 'T' Truths are about life and death."

"OK, give me your little 't' truth then," Hauser replies sarcastically.

"I don't think any human can know for sure what happens after death. From a medical standpoint, for example, we have stories about so-called near-death experiences in which people sometimes review their lives and have a sense of transcendence, but such stories may not tell us what death is actually like. We also have ideas from the world's wisdom traditions, such as rebirth, heaven, and hell."

"How can you seem so peaceful about death when you are so uncertain and confused?"

"I *am* uncertain about death, but *not* confused. Uncertainty is unavoidable in life, and when I accept uncertainty, then a little peace might come to me. It is only when I try to *avoid* uncertainty that I become confused, and that brings an inner conflict, which is the opposite of peace. Mr. Hauser, have you ever felt inner peace?"

"There is no such _____ thing as inner peace in this _____ up world!"

Three More Weeks Later, Deanna Bradley's Office

"Mr. Hauser, you called during the week and asked to come in early for your monthly session. What's up?"

"I'm not so sure anymore."

"About?"

"I'm not so sure anymore that I want to be immortal."

"Why?"

"Well, Doctor Yin told me that my body is responding well to the genetic treatments and that I am no longer aging, right?"

Deanna Bradley nods.

"So I will stay 59 years old forever, he said."

"Yes?"

"And the only way that I could die now is if there was an accident, or ..."

"Or?"

"Or if I ... you know ... took my own life."

"Has that thought crossed your mind?"

"If I say yes, then you'll tell the psychiatrist, and she will try to shrink me, right?"

"Well, if you tell me that you have suicidal ideation, I am required to note that in the file and ask you some questions, and yes, I would also have to bring this subject up in our staff meeting."

"There's something else," Billy J. says. "I am having these ... dreams."

"Yes?"

"Every night, the same _____ thing."

"Tell me what happens in the dream."

"Will you think I'm crazy?"

"You told me that you don't care what I think about you, remember? Has that changed?" Deanna notices that Mr. Hauser's hand is shaking slightly now.

"OK, I have this same dream, every night now, sometimes more than once. I am running away from something that is chasing me. It is dark out. I hear these footsteps getting closer and closer. I finally can run no longer, and I turn around to see what it is that's chasing me."

"Yes?"

"And it's me! I see myself! Am I going crazy?"

"No. But maybe you are going sane."

"What do you mean?"

"Let's try an experiment. I am going to put an empty chair in front of you. Let's pretend that the figure who is chasing you is now in that chair."

"I'm not sure I want to do any of your touchy-feely stuff now."

"Are you willing to just play with me for a few minutes? It might help."

"Uh ... OK."

"Now, I want you to sit in that chair please, Mr. Hauser."

Mr. Hauser gets up, walks over to the chair, and sits.

"Good, now I will sit in the chair that you just occupied, and I will pretend for a few minutes to be you, the dream figure who was being chased." She gets up and sits in the chair.

Deanna looks at Mr. Hauser. "I am *so* tired of running away from you. So I am ready to finally face you. Please tell me, why are you chasing me?"

Mr. Hauser looks very uncomfortable, his hands are shaking, and his eyes are a little wet.

"Uh ... I want you to stop and see me!"

"OK, what do you want me to see?"

"See that I'm ... I'm _____ miserable."

"Why are you so unhappy?"

"Maybe Sylvia was right. Maybe I am that man who never loses, but when I am not winning, that boredom does come back. But it's worse *than* boredom. I'm afraid I've somehow wasted my life, and now I have an eternity ahead of me—an eternity of more waste. I'm not sure anymore what is worse: living or dying."

Deanna walks back to her chair and leans forward toward Billy J. "Mr. Hauser, is it possible that a big part of why you wanted the immortality treatments is because you were hoping to have more time to get your life right?"

About Six Months after Mr. Hauser Began Treatments. Mount Tamalpais Cemetery

It is Sunday morning, and the ocean fog is wrapped around Mount Tamalpais so that it looks like an island floating in a white sea. Marin County residents voted to stop actual use of the grounds for burials back in the 2030s, but funerals are still held up on the famous mountain.

Three women stand together on the cement platform. The hospice chaplain is finishing her prayer. Sylvia is on one side of the small box of ashes and Deanna Bradley on the other. The chaplain continues.

"So only a few weeks after Ms. Dorothy Hauser died after her long battle with cancer, she is now joined in eternity by her son Billy James Hauser. We pray Lord that they both rest in everlasting peace. Amen."

"Amen," echo the two other women.

"Do either of you wish to speak?"

Sylvia, her eyes wet with tears, looks at the box of ashes that was once Billy J.

"Billy J., you were such a _____, and I loved you. I love you still. But you could never see that. Maybe because you actually never thought very much about yourself. I won't ever know why you had to kill yourself, I suppose, but my heart blames me. Did you kill yourself because you missed me? Goodbye, baby."

Deanna Bradley looks across the clouds to the west that stretch out as far as she can see out across the Pacific. In her mind, she muses, "A hundred years ago, Carl Jung said that when someone is suicidal, there is usually something in that person that actually needs to die. Billy J., you could not let go of that addiction you had to winning, to doing. And since you could not let that addiction die, you felt you needed to kill it, and you died trying.

"It makes me wonder if perhaps there is something we have neglected in the immortality program, something so essential that many more lives will be lost if we don't identify and address it."

CHAPTER 10

Interlude: The Child in the Mother-of-Us-All

Key themes in scenes:
1. The ability of a remarkable young woman to relate-effectively not only with other people but also with other living things
2. The possibility that such remarkable abilities, including the ability to achieve immortality, can be achieved by human beings through spiritual practice
3. All adults had a childhood that helped inform who they are today

Location: In the bush in what is now called Kenya
Date: November 13, about 200,000 years ago

They knew that the local lions usually would not pursue them up into the trees, especially into the higher branches, but they were ready in case this one was different.

And she was different.

Father motioned for Barannda's sisters and brothers to climb higher as he pointed the spear down at the approaching cat. He shouted at the lioness as she stared up at them, circling the base of the tree. He had not seen the animal before. Why was she walking alone without a pride? And there was something different about her. She was larger than most lionesses, and, yes, he could see in the dim dawn light that she had a mane, not as large as a male's, but it was as black as his own skin.

Barannda had climbed a tree nearby with her great-grandmother. They were picking berries, and there had not been enough time to stay with the rest of the family when they all heard the roar. Their tree was not as large as the tree that her father and siblings had climbed.

There was something different about her, too, this fourth daughter. Great-Grandmother and Father loved her as much as the others, but she looked, acted, and thought differently. From the moment she was born, they could tell.

Now the great lioness ran in great bounds over to the smaller tree where Great-Grandmother and Barannda were sitting up as high as they dared in the upper branches. Father knew he had to guard the children in his tree, and so he watched helplessly as the big lioness leaped easily up to the first horizontal branch. She opened her huge mouth and roared at the two women.

"Climb higher, Barannda!" cried Great-Grandmother. Instead, Barannda climbed slowly down toward the cat. She made the "pfft pfft" or puffing sound that the pride used to communicate peaceful intentions.

As the family watched in horror, Barannda slowly moved down to the branch that the lioness occupied. She continued to make the "pfft pfft" call softly to the cat.

The lioness responded, "Pfft pfft," and relaxed her ears, which she had pulled back. Barannda spoke to the lioness quietly and then the animal bounded suddenly off the tree to the ground and ran out of sight.

The family waited for a while and then gathered together again. Everyone had questions for Barannda,

"How did you save Great-Grandmother?"

"What gave you the courage?"

"What did you say to the cat?"

Barannda looked up at her great-grandmother. "I do not know. I had to do something. I felt an energy go through me, and I let that energy speak through me."

From that time on, everyone in the tribe described Barannda as a "Two Spirits" who had tamed the two-spirited lioness with a mane. Every generation or two, a child would be born who had both the feminine and masculine spirits. Since they were challenged to heal the feminine and masculine in their own lives, they were often selected to be the shamanic healers for the people as well.

Two Years Later, When Barannda Was Ten

Great-Grandmother was dying, or she seemed to be.

She had been Barannda's primary caretaker all of her life and was the most revered elder in the tribe. The tribal shaman was quietly chanting over her when Barannda came to visit. The sky was darkening and the "Sky's Spine" or Milky Way was already becoming visible above them.

Great-Grandmother reached her hand out to Barannda.

"Dear, Barannda, I have called you to the fire because I am ready to die now. As I have explained to you, death is life, and life is death. There is nothing to fear. Please hear me now, dear child. You have a task that Creator has given you. It will not be an easy task, but Creator will always be there for you. When you get yourself out of the way and let Her flow through you, She will tell you what to say and what to do."

"What am I to do, Great-Grandmother?"

Great-Grandmother spoke slowly while holding Barannda's hand. "Just like I have been your great-grandmother and just like I have been the great-grandmother for our people, you will become the great-grandmother for all the new people to come. You will have children, and their children will start to walk the earth. Your descendants will fill all the lands of this world with their children.

"Now look at this fire. Our descendants will learn how to use fire to do things we have never imagined. They will learn to fly like birds, and they will walk on that moon, yes. They will also use fire to kill each other and to destroy this beautiful planet."

"Why would they destroy our Earth?" Barannda asked.

"Because they will focus on their new power and their own greed, and forget who they are. As the grandmother of your new people, you will be there when the great Convergence happens, when the fire creators have the powers of life and death in their hands, and you will remind them of who we really are."

"When will this all happen, Great-Grandmother?"

"It will be about two hundred thousand years from now."

"But how will I live that long?"

"I will show you. It is possible to continue to live, to continue on, through our spiritual work. Now watch."

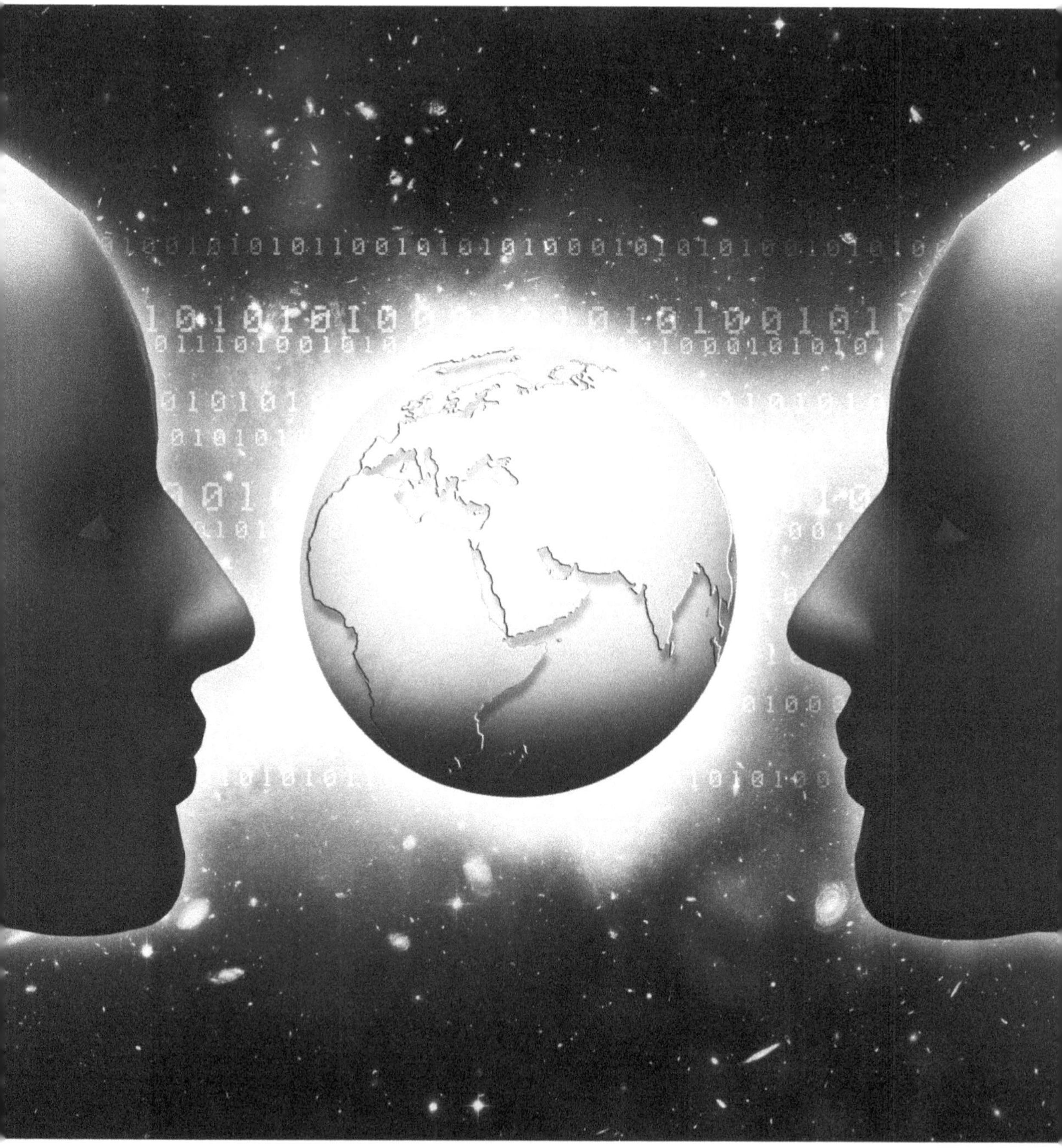

CHAPTER 11

Convergence

Key themes in scene:
1. Humanity has been moving toward an inevitable
"convergence" of global survival threats that finally build
to a major crises level in 2050
2. The Milky Way (or Sky's Spine) Galaxy is our home galaxy,
and our sun is one of billions of stars in that galaxy

Location: Loiyangalani on Lake Turkana, Great Rift Valley, Kenya
Date: June 21, 2050, after sunset

Still in the circle, the Great-Grandmothers share pieces of fried perch and vegetables as they now lay on their backs, watching the Milky Way reach across the dome of stars. The sky is dark in Northern Kenya at night, and the starlight is on all of their faces.

"We were taught to call it the Silver River back when I was a child, in what is now Vietnam," says Pham Ngoc while gazing upward.

"The Lake People called it 'Sky's Spine'" says Barannda Estava Maronna, "because it held up the sky. Now we women are called to hold up the sky for all the people on Earth."

"Yes, even though we knew that the Convergence was coming, it does not make it any easier," replies Pham Ngoc. "It is a great responsibility for us. We are few, and every day, there are more humans and more violence."

Barannda Estava Maronna sits up again and looks at all the faces now turned toward her. She recognizes the women's need to talk.

"Yes, we have much work to do this year. And that is why we have all chosen to do our spiritual work and to take many lives here on Earth. We come back again and again to be of service to our people, to all other living things, and to our Earth. We have kept our existence secret because our people were not ready yet to know. The time is coming when this will all change."

"Mother-of-Us-All," asks another great-grandmother, "will all people eventually become immortal like us?"

"Yes, that is our future, but immortality will not be achieved by technology alone. They are discovering that now. No technological shortcut can bring immortality without spiritual work."

"Mother," asks another, "have we already seen the worst of the Convergence?"

"We have seen the three technologies converge at the same time: intelligent robots, mental connectivity, and genetic immortality. All these technologies have the potential to link humanity together in peaceful and compassionate cooperation, and to also enable humans to further perpetuate violence on each other.

"Now we are entering a time of monologue. This is a time of rising violence, as humans compete to control their world through these technologies. Violence is always a monologue because the most vulnerable are always silenced, and the most powerful are always lost in their fear of those they oppress.

"We know that in every group, there is at least a small number of people who are doing their spiritual work. We will be offering assistance to this growing group of people who will help to transform humanity.

"We know that transformation is always possible in any lifetime. We also know that individual and collective transformation usually requires a crisis. The time of monologue is our people's biggest crisis—the biggest since the early days when our ancestors were struggling to survive in the drying savanna. Our big brains saved us then. Now our big brains threaten to kill us all."

Like a giant question mark looming above humanity, the Sky's Spine looks down on the circle of women.

Monologues and Demagogues

CHAPTER 12

Conversation on the Lake

Key theme in scene:
All people experience some self-doubt from time to time

Location: Loiyangalani on Lake Turkana, Great Rift Valley, Kenya
Date: June 27, 2050

Every human being, no matter how many strengths she may have, also has fear and self-doubt.

Barannda Estava Maronna walks along the shore of Lake Turkana. She looks again to the east; over her right shoulder is the outline of Mount Kulal in shadow from the first light of dawn. She hears the eagle owl still hooting as the stars slowly surrender to the growing light.

"Owl is good medicine for you" she remembers her great-grandmother telling her as they listened to the hooting on the lake together ages ago. "The owl is one of your spirit guides; she brings wisdom and the feminine ways of seeing. Whenever you hear her call, my spirit is close to you."

Barannda watches the rocky spot where the sun will emerge. She speaks aloud.

"Great-Grandmother, I need your help now. I have stayed here on this Earth for all these years as you asked me to do. My children and grandchildren have covered the earth, as you said, built their cities and their machines. Now the Convergence has begun, as you told me it would.

"I have learned to develop the spiritual powers that you taught me, and I am thankful. Yet I am human, with fear and self-doubt. My family now has ten billion children. So many now depend on me. So much to do. Sometimes, I feel so alone."

"You are never alone," says Misorri Estava Maronna, smiling as she puts her arm around her great-granddaughter's waist, "but since you were a little girl, you have often felt a separation from Creator. As I taught you, this was necessary. Your mental gifts came with an ego—an ego that tries to find substitutes for connection with the All."

As she comforts her granddaughter, Misorri Estava Maronna looks out at the emerging dawn. When they stand together, you can see that they share many common features, except the younger woman is much taller than her great-grandmother and has a larger head. In fact, Misorri liked to say when Barannda was a girl that she had a "big head," not only because of the physical size of her brain but also because Barannda was the first being on Earth born with an ego.

Misorri had sensed early on that Barannda's separate self was both a strength and a weakness. For example, on the one hand, even as a young child, Barannda could think for herself, change her behavior quickly in response to changes in the environment, and invent creative solutions to life challenges. However, on the other hand, since she had a persona, she also took things personally, compared herself to the other children, and suffered from a sense of shame.

In other words, it seemed to Misorri that Barannda's ego was a necessary part of the evolving consciousness of humans. She had watched Barannda separate from the oneness of creation to examine herself as an individual. She also could see in Barannda the birth of the ability to create the technologies of life and death. So she taught Barannda that the function of the ego is to lead us back to the One.

"As you know, child, when your mother died in childbirth, I took you on as my own." She continues, "The brain that Creator gave you made it hard on your mother during delivery, but I taught you that your mother gladly gave her own life so that you could live. Now it is time to use that brain.

"Yes, we live now in the time of Convergence, when humans have created the technologies of life and death, and now decide whether we will exist or not. Our existence depends on *how* we make this decision. Do we cooperate, or do we continue to hate and kill each other? This is the dangerous time when those in power tend to cling more and more desperately to the control they think they have and turn to violence as a means to keep the power they think they have. And violence, as I taught you when you were a child, is always a *monologue* because it refuses the voice of the Other."

Misorri stops, faces east, and raises her walking stick over her head. Standing together in the morning wind, she and Barannda see the first yellow-blue rays backlighting the mountain.

CHAPTER 13

Explosions

Key themes in scene:
1. Consequences of mass casualty terror
2. How wars often start

Location: Haikou, Hainan, 30 km from mainland China across the Qiongzhou Strait
Date: June 30, 2050

It is a lovely morning in Haikou, Hainan.

Yu Yan Zhou and her husband, Bo, are in the park near their home in Kaikou, Hainan. Since they retired, they come here every day to practice tai chi with other elderly people from the neighborhood.

There is a sudden flash of light in the southeast. Instead of subsiding, it grows larger. Then the sound of the explosion follows. Yu Yan and Bo both fall to the ground onto the wet grass. They watch a mushroom-shaped cloud rise over the trees near the Nandu River, maybe 15 or 20 km from where they lay.

The Chinese Defense Ministry estimates that the device has a yield of about 1–2 kt of TNT, maybe about one-twentieth the size of the bomb that destroyed Hiroshima in 1945. There are casualties, but the bomb explodes down-river from the city in a more rural area so that relatively few people are killed and injured.

Why would someone explode a nuclear bomb in rural China? The answer comes quickly in the form of a message received in the capitals of the Group of Thirteen economic powers of the world. The Global One takes responsibility for the attack and gives a warning. It is the voice of a lieutenant of Global One, distorted to protect his identity:

"To the wealthy nations of the world; it is time to take notice that the days of inequality are over. Our organization, Global One, has a stockpile of nuclear weapons and robot delivery systems, and we have just demonstrated that we are capable of exploding a device anywhere on the planet. China was targeted first since you are now the leading economic power and the biggest offender. Global One will give the Group of Thirteen ninety days to come with an international plan of redistribution of income and wealth. We also demand that you make the immortality treatments available to everyone at a reasonable cost. Finally, you must publicly recognize the problem of global warming and begin spending twenty-five percent of the gross national product on creating sustainable energy and industry. If this is not done, we will explode a much larger device, and this time it will be in the center of one of your major financial cities. Do not try to find us. If you do, there will be more terror attacks. We await your plan."

Location: Jakarta, Indonesia
Date: Four hours after the explosion

Mr. Kusumo, president of the Group of Thirteen, convenes an emergency simulacrum meeting from his office in Indonesia. The simulacrums of the other leaders sit around the image of a table in front of him. Kusumo looks at the visual representations of the leaders, and they see him through the eyes of their own simulacrums. The translation technology enables them to communicate in real time.

"Gentlemen and ladies, thank you for joining me for this emergency meeting. I presume you all have been briefed on the situation."

"The state chairman of China wishes to speak!" Chairman Lau's simulacrum stands up. "The great nation of China will not permit this cowardly attack on our homeland to go unanswered! How do we know this so-called terrorist attack is not just a cover for an attack from those of you in the world who are jealous of China's return to power and greatness? We are prepared to launch similar weapons on the homelands of all other nuclear powers unless we received cooperation in finding and destroying those who are responsible!"

"That is irrational!" President Sousa of Brazil responds. "Such actions would start a nuclear world war. Brazil is not responsible for your terror attack. We would retaliate, of course, and there would be no end to it!"

"Only an end to all of us," responds President Emily Browning. "Chairman Lau, we all understand how you must feel. I would be angry as hell if they had bombed a location in the United States. My intelligence service believes we may be able to locate this terrorist group and neutralize them before they act again."

Chairman Lau remains standing. "I will give you all one week to find these perpetrators, or China will act to defend itself."

"That is ridiculous!" President Çelik from Turkey screams. "It's not enough time!"

Location: Yellow Sea
Date: Twenty-four hours after the explosion

The Yellow Sea, only about 380,000 km² in area, is patrolled in 2050 by the militaries of six of the Group of Thirteen nations: Indonesia, China, Korea, Japan, Russia, and United States, as well as elements of the smaller navies of Taiwan, Vietnam, and the Philippines. Observation satellites have already picked up a threefold increase over normal military activity in the area. A Chinese carrier group, Korean sea robots (or ro-boats), and a fleet of missile cruisers from Japan have been deployed. Frigates from Russia and the United States are entering the sea. Heavy submarine activity from unidentified nations has also been detected, as well as active drone aircraft from all nine nations. The risk of accidental interactions is high.

One of the Korean ro-boats detects an attack from an unidentified aircraft. The biggest advantage and the biggest danger of artificial intelligence, or AI, war machines are perhaps their autonomy. Programmed to protect itself, the floating robotic boat fires antiaircraft missiles at the plane, which is actually a Chinese carrier jet dropping buoys for submarine detection. The Chinese plane is destroyed. The carrier group retaliates by sending out two frigates to destroy the Korean ro-boat. Korea scrambles land-based planes that attack the frigates. Many sailors and pilots on both sides are killed in the escalating exchange.

Location: Near Vladivostok, Russian Far East
Date: July 2, 2050

The general is one of the most respected in the Russian military. However, at 59 years old, General Pomsky is now looking over his shoulder as the younger officers who desire his position of chief officer of the Far East Theater. The way to security and advancement in the army has always been through victories in war. Perhaps the current crisis will lead to an opportunity for the general to become a war hero.

General Pomsky is proud of his new attack battalion. Along the Sino-Soviet frontier, the longest border in the world, the Russians have put their armies on high alert. Over the past decade, Russia has replaced most of its tanks with the battle robots they call "Putins." General Pomsky stands next to his new Putin D-29, the latest Soviet attack robot. His tech staffer, Sargent Krimton, take photos of the general, and then the robot walks off to join a column of other robots filing into the fir trees. Heading toward the Chinese frontier, they move quickly on their long niobium-fiber legs and soon disappear into the Taiga Forest.

The general walks over to his tech staffer and slaps him on the back.

"They're beautiful aren't they, Krimton? Sure hope we can test them out against those Chinese tanks this time; they won't know what hit them!"

Location: Washington, DC
Date: July 2, 2050

"I want to hear from both of you. Who goes first? Admiral Block or Dr. Reeves?"

President Emily Browning sits with her secretaries of defense and peace. When the president ran for the office, one of her campaign promises was to create a Department of Peace (DOP), which she did. Although funding for the new DOP is a tiny fraction of that of the Department of Defense, money was found for the salary for the first secretary of peace, Dr. Tasha Reeves.

Admiral Block speaks first, as he had grown accustomed to doing in his many years as director of National Space Defense. Talented and ambitious, Block had worked hard all his life to get to the top. He had experience working on a nuclear attack submarine and as an admiral of a carrier task force. He then served as director of the Space Defense Command, created in the 2030s to protect the country from attack from space. The president does not like him, but she was willing to acknowledge that Block knew more about advanced military systems than anyone else in the country.

"The Chinese are bluffing," he says confidently. "They know that none of us would deliver a bomb on their territory. This is some kind of power play, probably to justify their taking over control of the rest of the South China Sea and to test out our latest systems. In one day, they have already positioned their latest carrier fleet out there, almost as if they were planning this all along. Hell, *they* actually may be the ones who operate Global One! We cannot afford to let them control that sea. Almost forty-four percent of the world's shipping passes through that body of water!"

"Dr. Reeves?"

The new secretary of peace is a woman of mixed races and identities. Her father is a white man from San Diego and her mother a Navajo woman from New Mexico. She speaks slowly, as she learned to do as a child on the reservation.

"Madam President, every crisis, as the Chinese themselves said thousands of years ago, is an opportunity. In this case, an opportunity for peace. Instead of moving toward violent conflict, let's help the world see how we all share a common ground—a common purpose of protecting the planet we all love. We could go to the United Nations—even though it has become essentially more dysfunctional and powerless than ever—and ask for a meeting to be held there. Let's invite the Chinese and all the other nations in the South China Sea to a conference on peacemaking!"

"Tasha, thank God you don't have much of a budget yet, or you'd be talking about dropping rose petals from outer space down on the Chinese." Admiral Block turns to the president. "Madam President, we have one of our TrumpM200 series satellites in stationary orbit directly over the South China Sea. Give me the command, and I can have that station direct a high-energy laser onto their carrier and melt it into their sea in less than 30 seconds. They won't know what hit them!"

Location: Beijing, China
Date: July 2, 2050

Chairman Lau sits with his party bosses. It is not easy being the leader of the most powerful economy in the world; the more power you have, the more you have to look over your shoulder to watch those who resent your power. And he has many enemies now. Although the Communist Party still remains in control of China, the many people who have not benefited from the growth in the economic and military systems are becoming increasingly restless. Maybe a half-billion people, many of them living in poverty in the many huge cities, are angry and want a share of the wealth. In addition, the middle class, although larger than ever, continues to feel increasingly insecure and resentful of the lack of freedoms in the country.

Chairman Lau looks wearily across the table at the party bosses. He has only disdain for most of them. They kiss up to him all the time, but he knows they would all stab him in the back with a *dao* in a second if they could gain more power by doing so.

Party Minister Yin speaks first. He is one of the few who has the courage to be direct. "Chairman Lau and fellow party members, I am honored to speak with all of you. I am worried about our position. While I agree that we had to try to unite the country through fear of other nations, there are many risks to this strategy. After the military exchange in the Yellow Sea, we are on the brink of war with Korea, and although we have more bombs than they do, they only need a few to destroy our major cities."

There are murmurs of agreement across the table.

Chairman Lau stands up, raising his hand for silence. "Please, my friends, let me remind you all of what we are doing and why. As you all know, we are facing unprecedented domestic unrest. This is because of three main factors: the corruption in our ranks that leads to unequal distribution of wealth, the effects of capitalist propaganda through the global Internet, and rising tensions from our ethnic minorities. The best solution to all of these is to unite the masses through fear. *Fear*, my friends, is the source of power in any and every government. The capitalists use fear of individual economic failure to force their masses to conform to rigid work schedules. We are simply using the same fear of foreigners that our ancestors used so effectively to unite the country in past times of difficulty. We already have our media exchanges providing information about how the Koreans shot down our plane and how the Russians are positioning their war robots on our border."

General Guo raises his hand to speak. "Thank you, Chairman Lau, for your wise words and leadership. I wish to give a perspective from our great People's Army. The other powers do not know that we have developed a tiny yet mighty weapon system: our all-terrain Xi-bots. Thirteen hundred copies of our newest model, the

Xi-12, are positioned and ready for use in the Yellow Sea. These Xi-bots are the size of hummingbirds, yet they have a range of over one hundred kilometers and can carry conventional, nuclear, and high-energy weapons. They can fly and swim and even dive underwater for limited periods of time. They can be launched from planes, boats, and land. I strongly urge you to allow us to release all of these weapons on our enemies in the Yellow Sea. The Xi-bots will take their weapon systems by surprise, and China will once again rule the oceans. They won't know what hit them!"

CHAPTER 14

A Brave Young Woman

Key themes in scene:
1. A brave women's voice in her organization and
in service of the common good
2. Importance of the therapeutic relationship in counseling

Location: San Francisco, California
Date: July 2, 2050

Deanna Bradley walks up the ramp from the station downtown. She both enjoys and hates the ride in from her apartment in Oakland, across the Bay. In 2050, Bay Area Rapid Transit or BART uses the fast and quiet hydrogen-powered driverless trains that they pioneered in the 2040s. The new ticketless stations, powered by human footfalls on the kinetic floor tiles, are efficient but the people on the trains haven't changed a bit. Most of the other commuters seem to Deanna to be either silent and brooding, or impatient and unfriendly, or both.

She hears sirens outside, and when she emerges on Market Street, she finds herself in a melee of protestors and police fighting for control of the sidewalks. She edges her way around the crowd, trying to get to her office across the street.

Several people walk by her carrying a big sign that reads, "Immortality Belongs to Everyone, Not Just the Rich." Another sign says, "Greater Area Biotech's Immortality Is Immoral." When she gets to the door, she has to pass through a line of private security police who guard the entrance to Greater Bay Area Biotech. After scanning her eyes, they let her in.

The mood in the staffing room is tense and depressed. Randy Snyder is talking by headphone with his boss in Brazil as Deanna enters the room. Dr. Yin is whispering with Dr. Walker in the corner. The others are watching a news briefing about the unrest out on Market Street.

"Hello, everyone," Deanna says cheerfully, "it looks like folks have found out about us!"

Randy is focused on the images on his left glass lens and looks at Deanna with his dominant right eye as he grunts to her. Then he nods his phone off and stands up.

"OK, everyone here now? Let's begin. Apparently, there are protests going on in at least 18 other countries, and the situation is spreading. I just spoke with Lucus, and he wants us to release the same statement to the press that they are using in Brazil. I will read it to you:

"Greater Bay Area Biotech is very proud of our affiliation with Bi2 or Biotech Industries International. Our corporate policy is to provide the highest quality, safest, and most affordable medical technologies on the planet. Bi2 has spent enormous sums of money to develop and test our immortality treatments, and while we understand that people want to have free access to the treatments, such technologies, unfortunately, do not come for free. We are doing everything we can to reduce the costs of the treatments. In the meantime, we ask everyone to please remain calm and to be patient. Thank you."

"But that is a lie." Everyone turns to look at Deanna, who sits uncomfortably in her chair. "We all know that Bi2 has inflated the price of the treatments and that they rushed the product to production without testing it properly. That's why we did not expect these suicidal reactions."

The room is silent.

"Miss Bradley," replies Dr. Yin sternly, "perhaps if you are unhappy with your job here at Greater Bay Area Biotech—"

"Dr. Yin, is that a threat?"

"Uh, no, of course not, my dear," says Randy Snyder. "We appreciate your youthful enthusiasm. It is just that there are certain uh ... issues that the public is not ready to hear. You are a wonderful asset to the company, and your patients give you the highest satisfaction ratings."

Randy looks around the room. "We *all* need to focus on our work. Management thinks that the protests will soon quiet down. They asked me to let you all know that you will each be receiving a bonus commensurate with your salaries."

There is applause in the room, and Randy notices that Deanna, once again, is the only one who is not applauding.

One Hour Later

Deanna walks out to the waiting room to meet Mrs. Emily Schmucklehauser. Deanna does not enjoy the staff meetings, and that last one was especially annoying. She does, however, still love her clients, and Emily is one of her favorites.

Deanna feels that one of the most important things she learned in graduate school was the importance of the therapeutic relationship. Not that intervention theories and methods are unimportant; the social worker has to do *something* when she is with the client. It is just that, as her favorite professor always said, if you don't genuinely love your clients and show the clients that you love them, you will ultimately not be very effective.

Deanna liked Emily from the first time they met. She reminded her of her great aunt Becky because both are outspoken and strong women. She smiles when she reflects on her old social work professor, Dr. Dave, who reminded students that people tend to make their minds up about others in less than one minute and that most of what we think about others is projection. She also remembered that social workers can have two kinds of countertransference, reactions to their clients: underidentification and overidentification.

"I have an overidentification with Mrs. Schmucklehauser" she thinks to herself, "which means I will tend to overemphasize our similarities and underemphasize our differences."

"Hello, Emily, please come back." She escorts Emily to the counseling room.

When the women are seated, Deanna asks, "How are you today?"

"Well, Deanna, I am feeling a little guilty."

"Why?"

"I've been watching the news. I feel bad because I'm able to afford the immortality treatments, and so many other people cannot."

"I understand. I like it that you are concerned about others who are less fortunate than you, but I am not sure that your guilt will help any of them. What if you tried thinking about how you could be response-able instead?"

"What do you mean?"

"I mean, what if you thought about what the best *response* is that you are *able* to have in this situation. What could you do that would make you feel best about yourself?"

"OK. Yes, I was thinking about this because I knew you would give me this advice. It's like I have my social worker in my head now," Emily says with a smile. "I decided this week that I could buy a treatment sequence for someone who cannot afford it! My husband, Bill, left me a large inheritance. I can afford to do this. And, Deanna, can I bring up something else?"

"Of course."

"You know, I just turned 70 last year. The doctors told me from the start that the treatments cannot make the body younger; they just stop the aging process where it is at. Yet I find myself longing for my 30-year-old body. Deanna, I want to love again. I want to start another career. But my 70-year-old body is not as enthusiastic as I would like it to be."

Deanna leans back in her chair. One of her gifts is that she can quickly imagine what it is like to be another person. Dr. Dave used to quote the famous American actor Robin Williams who said that a therapist and an actor do the same thing. They both imagine the other.

"Emily, that has to be frustrating. After an unhappy marriage and years of exasperation because your writing career never took off, you spend all this time and money on the immortality treatments only to feel unsatisfied again."

Emily nods slowly, looking down at her wrinkled hands folded in her lap. "Deanna, I wonder sometimes if this is all a mistake. Maybe this immortality you have created is something you should only sell to the young, and yet they might not appreciate it like I do. When you are 25, you don't think about death; it's like you think you are immortal."

"Do you think about death?" Deanna asks.

"Yes, every day, but not in a gloomy way. I think about it in a *spiritual* way, as we started to talk about the last time we met."

"Did you have time to think about what spirituality means to you?"

"Yes, after you asked me that question, you suggested that I start to journal. I went and bought a nice journal unit and started to talk to it every evening. It was different. I was not journaling to try to publish something but just doing it for myself. And I found myself reflecting on how when I feel the most spiritual, I feel *linked with and related to* everything else. That's why I feel guilty ... no ... *sad* that other people can't afford the immortality treatments."

"Emily, would you like to go deeper into all of this?"

"Yes. I want to understand myself. I want to know what I really want."

"Wonderful. Let's start by looking at the person inside of you whom you want to live forever, to love again, to have a second career."

"What do you mean?"

"Remember when we talked about the differences between heart, head, and ego?"

"Yes. Emotions come from the heart, thoughts from the mind, and ego is the identification with thought and belief."

"Yes. So which of those voices in you wants immortality?"

"I suppose it is a little bit of all three. My heart *wants* love and vocational success. There's nothing wrong with that right?"

"Right."

"And my mind says that I *should* have these things in my lifetime."

"Good. That is your conditioning, of course."

"Yes. And my ego *identifies* with the belief that I deserve to have love and vocational success in my lifetime."

"Good, and as we look at these things together, right now, in this office, what happens?"

Emily smiles. "Well, I don't feel as angry as I did a few minutes ago. I am not as identified with the thought that I *must* have love and vocation to be happy. In fact, I feel more connected again. Is it possible that I am feeling spiritual again?"

Deanna smiles back. "What do you think, Emily?"

Location: Oakland, California
Time: 6:00 p.m. that evening

Deanna takes the long way home, walking from the station through the park near her apartment as she reflects on her day. Her cat, Billy, hears her walking up the back stairs and is waiting at the door for her as her face is scanned and the lock opens.

"Hey, Billy. I'll get you fed in a minute, little dude."

Her phone activates and she says, "Hello?"

"Deanna? This is Charlie Fellis from the *San Francisco Chronicle* returning your call."

"Yes, Mr. Fellis. Thank you for calling. I think I have a story for you. You see, I work for Bay Area Biotech."

"Can we meet somewhere?" Mr. Fellis asks.

"Yes. I live near the UC Berkeley campus. Is that possible?"

"I can be there in an hour."

Location: Coffee shop, Main Library, UC Berkeley campus
Time: 7:00 p.m.

Mr. Fellis is a small man with a big smile and a bigger heart. His father was of European descent, and his mother's family was from Columbia. He leans back in his chair and sips some more coffee. The coffee is so weak and tasteless compared to his beloved Columbian coffee. He looks at Deanna.

"Deanna these are serious charges that you're making about Greater Bay Area Biotech and about their parent company, Bi2. Do you realize that they may do something to retaliate if they learn that you gave me this information?"

"Yes," says Deanna, swallowing down a little fear. "They probably want to fire me anyway. I was worried because it is my first job, but it is not worth it anymore. I want the public to know what is going on. Maybe the government can do something to regulate this industry before they cause more harm."

Location: School of Social Welfare, UC, Berkeley
Time: Early the next morning

Deanna sits across from her former professor in his tiny office in Haviland Hall. The bus was late, and she is still out of breath after running past the familiar old campus redwood trees in the rain to get to his office on time.

"Thank you for seeing me at the last minute, Dr. Dave."

Dr. Dave is a small aging professor who still manages to teach the practice classes at the school. "No problem. It's good to see you. So, how's it going Deanna?"

"Not so great I'm afraid," Deanna responds. She tells Dr. Dave her story about taking the job at Greater Bay Area Biotech, how her first client had killed himself, and how the management responded to her concerns.

"Well, I'm proud of you regarding both how you worked with the client and that you stood up to the management, but the experience may have taken a toll on you. Remember how we talked in class about how it is easy to take on shame when people shame us? Do you think it is possible that your own shame has been reactivated in this experience?"

Deanna's eyes tear up. "Yes. It is *very* possible."

Dr. Dave leans forward. "You were one of my best students, so I think you may remember when we studied Noam Chomsky's ideas, written back around 2018, about, as he put it, 'who rules the world?'"

"Yes, I do,"

"Great. Do you remember what he said about the two kinds of intellectuals?"

"Hmm ... yes. There are the folks who do not know how to lead, and Chomsky said that they often become regulators, and they rule the world. And the folks he called the 'value-based' intellectuals he said actually may help make the most positive and significant changes, but they may also end up in jail!"

"And why do the regulators rule the world?"

"Because that is what the most powerful people want them to do. They emphasize that things in the organization should appear at least to be running smoothly. Profit, wealth, and power are their highest values. The regulators are willing to regulate, so that they can have a share of power, which gives them a temporary sense of pleasure. Unfortunately such power, power over others, is not deeply satisfying, so the pursuit of such power can become addictive."

"Yes!" Dr. Dave says. "And why do the value-based intellectuals often get in trouble?"

"Because they are truth tellers?"

"Yes! And which of those two groups do you put yourself in?"

Deanna smiles. "I am value based because I value telling the truth. I value the highest good of my clients over the corporate goals of wealth and power. Thank you, Dr. Dave, for helping me see that I did the right thing."

"You are welcome. And, of course, you figured that out by yourself, Deanna. Remember, that is what education is really about; we don't offer so-called knowledge to people so we can test them on that knowledge later. Instead, we draw out what people already know inside themselves. Where are you going?"

Deanna is already standing and putting on her jacket.

"I've got to get to work. Thanks again for helping me remember who I am really am!"

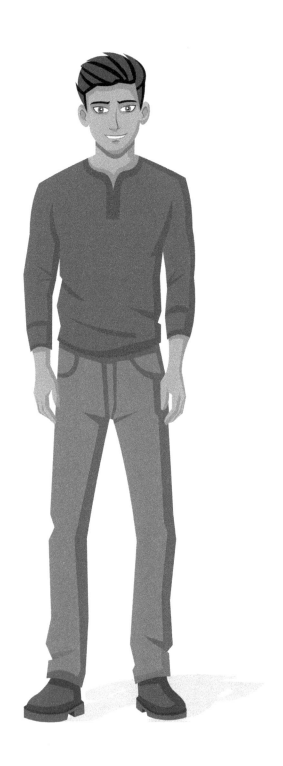

CHAPTER 15

Interlude: A Brave Young Man

Key themes in scene:
1. One brave person can make a difference in any organization
2. When in doubt about what to do, show
loving kindness toward other people

Location: Washington, DC
Date: June 22, 2050

Jean-Paul feels like he has the world on his shoulders. In a sense he does.

His fellow lieutenants in Global One had given him only one week to contact the CEOs and arrange some kind of nonviolent solution to the growing inequities in the world. The problem was real enough: whereas in 2018, about one-half of the world's wealth was controlled by the richest 1 percent of the population, that group now controlled two-thirds of global wealth in 2050. However, Jean-Paul knew in his heart and mind that violence would not solve the problem.

Now he sits with Dmytro at their favorite spot near the Lincoln Memorial Reflecting Pool.

"Dmytro, I love you, but you are wrong about this."

"Let's not get into it again, my brother," replies Dmytro.

Jean-Paul looks across the water at Lincoln's statue. His thoughts drift. He has not seen any of his biological family since they had been taken away by the soldiers, years ago, when he was a child in Colombia. He was a sophomore at National University of Colombia in Bogotá when he first met Dmytro. Now Dmytro has become the brother he never had.

They have things in common. Dmytro was an exchange student who grew up in an orphanage in Ukraine. Jean-Paul's father left his mother before he was born. She raised him and his older sister by herself. Both are dissatisfied with the governments of their home countries and both desire radical change. Now they live together, like brothers, in a small apartment in Columbia Heights, northwest Washington, DC, where they coordinate their Global One organization.

They have differences. Dmytro is emotional with a quick temper and often impulsively takes action before he thinks much about the possible outcomes of his decisions. Jean-Paul is more logical, self-controlled, and tends to overthink things before he acts.

Jean-Paul knew that a week would probably not be enough time to arrange a meeting with GMU, much less influence the company to agree to terms. He also knew that he would be in grave danger if he contacted GMU directly, because they would be likely to detain and probably even torture him to get information. But he had to do something to try to stop Global One from detonating a bomb and killing innocent people.

He comes up with a plan. It is risky, but it seems to offer some chance of success. It is too dangerous for him to visit GMU in person. But he knows that one of the war robots that Global One purchased has been sent to DC to be positioned for a possible attack. He has to first locate the robot and then take control of it without alerting anyone in Global One. He can't even tell Dmytro because doing so will put his friend in a difficult loyalty conflict between Global One and himself.

"I do have a plan, my brother."

"Well," responds Dmytro grimly, "I hope it works for your sake and for the sake of everyone."

They shake hands. That will be the last time that Jean-Paul sees his brother alive.

Location: Washington, DC
Date: June 28, 2050

The robot is about 6 feet tall and in a suit and tie. It appears to be a well-dressed man. It walks up to the entrance to the national office of GMU located in downtown Washington, DC, and presses the red "talk" button by the door.

Sitting in a coffee shop a block away, Jean-Paul looks through the robot's eyes from his communication device built into his sunglasses. He drove the robot into downtown Washington, DC, in his Toyota this morning. The robot sat obediently in the front seat as Jean-Paul found a parking spot in a garage. He knew that the robot was designed to operate autonomously on the battlefield, but he did not trust the robot to handle this conversation. He decided to run the robot manually. He had the robot walk at a normal human pace to the GMU offices.

Now he watches as 12A19 is finally greeted by a GMU guard robot at the door. Jean-Paul's robot speaks slowly to the guard robot.

"Hello. I am one of the war robots, model 12A19, purchased by Global One from one of your agents in the Crimea. I am here to negotiate a deal with your organization. I have digital proof of my identity."

The guard robot contacts Mr. Henry Gladstone upstairs, the director of the Washington, DC, GMU office. About 30 minutes later, 12A19 is in a secured room upstairs, surrounded by armed guards. Mr. Gladstone enters the room perspiring.

"Well, our national office has confirmed that you are one of the missing robots. We are interested in hearing what you have to tell us."

Protected by its hafnium-vanadium shielding, 12A19 believes that the human guards cannot cause it any harm. It speaks again. "I come to make you an offer. As you know, Global One now has a supply of weapons produced by your industries that can cause vast destruction. However, we are a peaceful organization that does not wish to harm any human being. We have a list of demands that I will be downloading for you in a minute. Essentially, they require that you redistribute ninety-eight percent of your wealth to poor people across the world."

"And if we refuse?" asked Gladstone.

"We will let the world know that a representative of GMU sold us these weapons. And two more things, Mr. Gladstone. First, do not try to harm or restrain me or any human in Global One. Second, any duplicity on your part will result in dire consequences."

"Understood. I will contact my superiors and have an answer for you as soon as possible. Would you remain here until then?"

"Agreed."

Jean-Paul smiles grimly to himself as he watches the exchange between the robot and Gladstone. He did not expect that the robot would be allowed to leave, so he had directed it to self-destruct upon his instructions, or in three hours, whichever came first.

Jean-Paul grows increasingly nervous. What are they doing?

Suddenly, the transmission from the robot is interrupted by a loud noise and then there is silence. Jean-Paul is unable to recontact 12A19, so he calls Dmytro.

"Hello?"

"Hello, this is Dmytro. To whom do I have the pleasure of speaking?"

With his heart beating wildly now, Jean-Paul realizes instantly that the voice is not that of his brother. But who is speaking? Something is seriously wrong. If he stays on the line, they can trace him. They may already be sending robots after him. He closes the phone and walks slowly out of the coffee shop two blocks from the GMU offices and down into a subway entrance. Up above him, he can hear sirens.

Location: Washington, DC
Date: June 29, 2050

Jean-Paul sits with his fellow revolutionaries again. A tall thin white man from Sweden named Alex is speaking.

"As far as we know, Dmytro was ambushed and killed in a firefight yesterday. Four more of our brothers died in attacks last night in Mexico and Iran. The 12A19 was deactivated and its memory has probably been retrieved. Jean-Paul, your efforts have failed. You may have put us all in increased danger. They probably are tracing the robot's activity map and soon may be bursting into this apartment as well. I am now taking over Global One. We will be moving our headquarters to Australia within the week."

Heads nod in agreement. The room feels tense. Only Jean-Paul shakes his head in disagreement.

Alex continues, "Enough talk. It is time to strike them. Let's start with China, the biggest offender."

Jean-Paul sadly replies, "You are correct that my efforts failed, but we all knew that the chances of success were small. We also know that their agents have been closing in on us for some time now. Dmytro told me two days ago that he thought he was being followed when he was in Canada. What is important is that we limit the loss of life. If you must strike China, please strike in a rural area with a small device and limit casualties. Remember that anytime you set off a nuclear device, you will harm many of the people we say that we are striving to protect. History has shown that mass casualty terror attacks always fail. The famous 911 attack in New York, for example, killed thousands of innocents and united much of the world against the terrorists."

A few heads nod, and Jean-Paul hopes that they are considering his words.

Location: Washington, DC
Date: June 30, 2050

Jean-Paul sits at a table with three men, all dressed in conservative suits. Behind him stand two armed military robots.

The door opens and a woman walks in. She extends a hand to Jean-Paul, who stands up to shake it.

"Mr. Martinez, I am Dr. Tasha Reeves, secretary of the United States' Department of Peace."

"Thank you for meeting with me Madam Secretary!"

They both sit down. Dr. Reeves motions to the robots, and they back away and lower their weapons. Although frequently accused of being a "tree hugger" and a "softy" by her critics, Dr. Reeves has a strong and commanding personality, and most people who meet her quickly have a sense that she is quite assertive, intelligent, and perceptive.

"You are welcome," she replies. "My people have checked out your story, and they have confirmed that you are one of the founding members of Global One. It took courage for you to come here unarmed. You know that there are many people in Washington who would be happy to get their hands on you, and they would go to any lengths to extract information from you about your organization."

"Thank you, Madam Secretary. And you are a brave woman to take on the role of secretary of peace in this violent world."

Dr. Reeves offers a small smile.

Jean-Paul continues, "I hoped that I might be able to trust you. If you would allow me, I want to get to the point. We do not have much time. I would like to do what I can to help resolve the crisis that we are all in, which I am afraid I have played a part in creating."

"What is your motivation for doing this? We know your coleader Dmytro Bondar was recently killed by security forces. I would imagine that you would be more motivated by revenge at this moment than by love."

"Madam Secretary, I loved Dmytro as a brother, and yes, I am angry and sad that he was killed. I also disagreed with him often about the strategies that Global One should take. When he was killed, I was blamed for his death, and a new group of young men took over the leadership of Global One. I am afraid they are as violent as Dmytro was and perhaps more impulsive. They are planning to explode a nuclear device somewhere in China, and I did everything I could to get them to explode the device away from people."

"So what do you propose?" Dr. Reeves asks.

"To work together to find a peaceful resolution. And there must be many others in the world like us who want to find nonviolent solutions to our global challenges."

"Yes, Mr. Martinez, there are many like us. We may not have political power yet, but we have empowerment, which is to say that we know what we think and feel and express those thoughts and feelings effectively."

"Yes. I fear that a nuclear explosion will start an acceleration of violence that none of us can stop. I just hope it's not too late."

One of the aides, after listening to his communication device interrupts. "I'm afraid that it *is* too late. Madam Secretary, we just learned that a nuclear device was exploded in southern China a few minutes ago."

CHAPTER 16

CEOs, Scientists, and Ordinary People

Key themes in scene:
1. The increasing corporatization of the University
2. The whistle-blower role, again

Location: Incheon National University Incheon, Korea
Date: July 1, 2050

As the receptionist walks in, Dr. Jiu Kang sits in the waiting room of the office of the vice president for research at Incheon National University in Korea.

"Dr. Kang? The vice president is ready for you now."

Dr. Kang walks into Vice President Park's office, which is second in size only to the president's office down the hall. Dr. Park is sitting with two well-dressed men.

"Dr. Kang, let me introduce you to Mr. Smythe and Mr. Brocktone from Global Multinationals Unlimited."

Following the conventional handshakes, they all sit down.

Vice President Park smiles warmly. "Dr. Kang, I am very pleased to let you know that Mr. Smythe and Mr. Brocktone are going to be funding your work on the development of a new worldwide Mental Web at Communication Technology Lab for years to come!"

Dr. Kang does not show any emotion on her face as she replies, "Vice President Park, we had an understanding that the research team wanted to develop this technology independent of any outside interests so that our work could benefit all of mankind."

Vice President Park smiles as he replies, "Dr. Kang, Global Multinationals Unlimited is also giving us a very generous donation for several new buildings on campus, including a new technology center that your team will be able to use, which will be named Global Multinationals Institute. These donations total about

330.9 trillion won. We all need to be grateful to and cooperative with our new corporate sponsors."

Everyone is smiling at the table, except for Dr. Kang.

Location: Salt Lake City, Research Park, University of Utah
Date: July 1, 2050

"But that's not fair!"

Phil Parker sits with his colleagues in their lab in Research Park. The simulacrums of their colleagues at Incheon National University, Korea, and at the University of Lorraine in Nancy, France, are also projected in the room.

Dr. Jiu Kang has just explained to everyone how GMU has taken control of their research project, based at Inchon.

Dr. Adele Dubois is quite upset. "Isn't there something we can do?"

"I'm afraid that since the study is based at Incheon National University, there is little we can do. I have been told that our research is owned by the university and that an agreement with GMU has already been signed and approved."

Phil and his project supervisor, Marge Sommers, look at each other. Although the part their team is playing in the development of the Mental Web is relatively small, they are both surprised and disappointed by the news. Based in Incheon and to a lesser degree in France, the Mental Web project includes scientists and technicians in another four universities in the USA, Brazil, Poland, and Iran. They suspect that everyone will probably be affected by this new development. They just don't know what that impact will be.

Phil raises his hand. "What if we go public?"

"What do you mean?" asks Dr. Kang.

"What if we hold a press conference and let people know that GMU has purchased control of the project? They are already under considerable scrutiny about the profits they are making from their immortality treatments. Perhaps even more public pressure will force them to back down. Most people probably resent the power they have over their lives already and the wealth they have accumulated."

"If we do that, we could all lose our jobs," says Dr. Dubois.

"But if we don't, the risk is far greater," responds Dr. Kang sadly.

Location: West Valley City
Date: July 1, 2050, three hours later

Phil Parker is still angry about the meeting at work today. He has always been an idealist and doesn't like being told "no" by anyone. When he gets home, Sid has dinner ready as usual. The family sits down to eat, and Sid turns on the TeleTouch.

"I wonder what new terrible news we will see tonight," quips Sid's son Frederick.

It does not take long to find out.

"And now from our new affiliate in San Francisco, we have a segment from a press conference staged by an employee of Greater Bay Area Biotech, an affiliate of Global Multinationals Unlimited, the owners of the new immortality treatments."

The simulacrums of Deanna Bradley and Charlie Fellis appear above the table.

"Good evening. I am Charlie Fellis from the *San Francisco Chronicle*. I am honored to be sitting with a brave woman I just met last night who has decided to step forward and blow the whistle on Greater Bay Area Biotech and their parent corporation, the gigantic Global Multinationals Unlimited."

Deanna nods nervously at Charlie. "Thank you, Mr. Fellis. I am a social worker currently employed by Greater Bay Area Biotech, although I do not know how much longer I will have my position. I decided to go public with what I have to say not because of any animosity toward my employer but because of my ethical responsibility as a social worker and my compassion for my clients and the general population.

"There are two things I want to tell you all. First, the immortality treatments are psychologically and spiritually difficult for most people, and this fact has been hidden from the public. Common side effects include depression, anxiety, and suicidal ideations. I was assigned to work as a social worker with the first people to receive the immortality treatments in the United States. I have, therefore, gotten to know these people very well. We don't understand yet all the reasons for these difficulties. I am concerned that powerful psychotropic medications are being prescribed for our patients but the root causes of the psychological difficulties and potential remedies have not yet been adequately studied.

"Second, a tremendous amount of money is being made through the sale of these treatments to wealthy people, which as you know limits the availability of the treatments for people who are not so wealthy. The company could afford to offer these treatments for far less money. In addition to this lack of economic justice, I am also concerned that the profit motive may be blinding the corporation I work for to their ethical responsibilities to be transparent with the public about what is going on."

The images shift as the announcer breaks in. "We have in our studio Randy Snyder, the clinic manager of Greater Bay Area Biotech. Mr. Snyder, thank you for agreeing to participate in this conversation tonight. You just listened to Deanna Bradley. These are serious charges. Any comments?"

"Thank you for inviting me. Although I did not know what would be said tonight, I do have a prepared statement from our office for you." Randy Snyder looks down at a sheet of paper and reads the statement.

"Global Multinationals Unlimited is committed to offering the world's highest quality biotechnological treatments to people around the world. We maintain the highest standards of research and treatment protocols. We do everything possible to offer our products and services at the lowest prices possible, but our rising research and development costs demand that we set prices that offset these costs. Thank you."

The announcer's voice returns. "And now for other news, the state of Puerto Rico is implementing the latest anti-hurricane technology to disrupt Hurricane Duane, which is approaching the Caribbean this week."

Phil turns down the volume and leans back in his chair. He looks at Sid.

"Wow, that woman has courage. Makes me want to do the same thing. You know, I had a dream this past week. I dreamed that I was at work, frustrated with the bureaucracy as usual. There was an announcement that we had hired a new leader for our unit and that he was coming in to clean things up. At that moment, the door opens, and everyone starts to applaud as the new hire walks in. I look up and see that the 'new' person is me."

Location: Salt Lake City, *Salt Lake Tribune* offices, downtown
Date: July 2, 2050

"What am I doing?" Phil Parker asks himself under his breath as he sits nervously in the reception area.
"Mr. Parker? Please come in."

Phil follows the receptionist past the security wall and back to the desk of reporter Doris Delora.

"Delora, this is Mr. Parker."

As they shake hands, Phil is immediately impressed with Delora's warmth. He had often read her online articles. After the *Trib* finally went completely online, he had continued a subscription in part because of her courageous reporting. Now it was his turn to be courageous, he thought.

"Thank you for meeting with me, Ms. Delora. I have admired your work for a long time. I have a story for you and would like to remain an anonymous source if that is possible."

"Thank you, Mr. Parker. And yes, please go on."

"There is a corporate takeover going on regarding the new Mental Web technology being developed primarily in Korea that the public needs to be aware of. Global Multinationals Unlimited, or GMU, has purchased the rights to the Mental Web research done at a number of public universities. What this means is that a safe and simple technology that would essentially connect everyone on the planet for free is now owned by the most powerful and wealthy corporate group in the world."

130

DOMINIQUE de LA ROCHEFOUCAULD,   JEAN JACQUES POUPART,   CHRISTOPHE de BEAUMONT,

CARDINAL, ARCHEVÊQUE de ROUEN, ABBÉ de CLANY et de FÉCAMP.   CURÉ DE St EUSTACHE, CONFESSEUR du ROI LOUIS XVI   ARCHEVÊQUE de PARIS, DUC et PAIR de FRANCE.

Dessinés d'ap. Nature par Trayes vers 1776.

CHAPTER 17

The Clerics, the Heyoka, and a Great-Grandmother

Key themes in scene:
1. Once again, the power of one brave individual to help make a community transformation
2. Leadership of older women in the community

Location: Todaiji in Nara, Japan
Date: July 1, 2050

Pope Luca walks up to the microphone. Gone is the enthusiasm he had when as this year's host he welcomed everyone to the first day of the 2050 World Summit of Religious Leaders. The stress of the last week shows on his face and in his voice.

"Good morning, everyone. I want to thank all of you who were able to extend your stay at the summit here in Nara for a few more days. We are all aware that the world is in a crisis. No doubt God planned that we would be meeting when these events occurred so that as religious leaders, we could work together to save humanity.

"We decided last night to continue our conversations today and have an open microphone for any committees or individuals who wish to speak. We will also be taking calls from our colleagues across the world who were unable to be here today.

"I understand that the Apocalypticism Committee wants to speak first. We recognize the chair of that committee, the Reverend Willy Mandly."

"Thank you, Pope Luca. Fellow believers, the apocalypse is coming, and soon we will all be reunited with our Lord! We have seen all the signs that are predicted in our holy texts. We are issuing calls to our followers all over the world to prepare themselves. This evening, we invite all of you to join us in a prayer session in the main garden after dinner."

There is applause and the entire auditorium is filled with talk. Some clerics stand up to cheer.

"Thank you, Reverend Mandly," says the pope.

A number of hands go up, and several people walk up to the open microphone.

"Praise to God!" exclaims one member of the clergy. "I recommend that we disband this conference, all go home, and make peace with God before the end comes!"

More applause. The sound of many side conversations fills the hall.

Another clergy member walks up, and she echoes the same themes.

In the turmoil, no one seems to notice a small thin man walking up to the microphone. His skin is dark brown, and he wears a long ponytail. Around his neck hang beaded symbols of the raven and coyote, swinging next to the security photo badge everyone at the summit must wear.

The pope hesitates, studying the face of the man on the screen in front of him. "Yes, sir? I don't think we have met."

"Good morning. No, sir, we have not met. My name is Billy Lee. I am Oglala Lakota. My people live in the Pine Ridge district in what the white man now calls South Dakota. I am recognized as heyoka and have served my people's spiritual needs all my life."

He looks around the room slowly and then with a straight face says, "All this talk of the end of the world makes me mighty uncomfortable since I was planning to go on a nice vacation down in Vegas this summer."

There is a slight ripple of embarrassed laughter in the hall.

Billy Lee then smiles warmly. "My people are concerned. We think that we have not taken care of our Mother, that is Mother Earth. We have taken everything from Her and given little back. However, Mother Earth will not die; we humans do not yet have the power to destroy the planet. We do have the power to destroy ourselves.

"As you may know, we First Nations people have stories about the apocalypse too, including those of the Seneca and Paiute. However, even if an end is coming, we do not believe that Creator wants us to stop taking up the responsibility we have. As spiritual leaders, we are charged with caring for all people. All this talk of the apocalypse can lead to more escapism at the very time when we could be working together to create peace in our human world."

Now there is an even louder conversation in the hall. Shouts of "blasphemy!" erupt from the back. Once again, Pope Luca hesitates, uncertain about what to do. The man has a point, but the Apocalypticism Committee is very powerful, and the pope will soon have to run again for the position of summit leader. He decides to interrupt Billy Lee and asks the security robots to escort him back to his seat.

Billy Lee walks calmly with the robots. He can see the pope's emotions, knows that resistance at this point would not be helpful, and hopes there will be another opportunity to talk.

The Apocalypticism Committee submits a proposal that the summit publicly endorse a statement that they have prepared:

Today, humanity is faced with a crisis of monumental proportions. Apocalypse is coming. We, the World Summit of Religious Leaders believe that God has created this crisis to prepare us for the last days. We are being warned that we all need to renew our commitment to our faith. Only those who believe will be saved in the next life, soon to come.

Later that evening, the membership votes to support the position of the Apocalypticism Committee, and participants make travel arrangements to return to their homes and prepare.

Location: Todaiji in Nara, Japan, in the Nara Gardens
Date: July 1, 2050, five hours later

A small group of clergy members sit in a circle while the chair of the Social Action Committee, Pastor Larah Jones, speaks.

"Thank you for coming to this meeting. We are all part of the committee that has met at the summit for the past few years. This evening, I would like to open up the meeting and let people talk about how they think and feel about what happened today."

Pastor Ravis speaks first. "I was quite unhappy that the summit was taken over by the Apocalypticism Committee and particularly disappointed at how Pope Luca caved in to them. I am not saying that some kind of disaster is not in store for humanity. But I am agreeing with what our new friend Billy Lee said today: that even if an end is coming, we can't give up on the world; we have to keep trying, and we have to do what we can *now* to care for our sisters and brothers."

Two more people walk in. The committee members recognize Billy Lee, who they saw speaking earlier today at the summit. He is accompanied by an older woman who is wearing a simple sari.

Pastor Jones stands up and offers her hand to Billy. "I am Pastor Jones. Thank you for coming to our meeting, Mr. Lee. We are honored. And thank you for your words today."

Billy holds the pastor's hand for a moment and then gestures to his companion. "Pastor, let me introduce you to my teacher, Aaradhya Sargretti from New Delhi, India."

As the pastor takes the old woman's hand, she is immediately struck by the remarkable combination of warmth and power in her eyes.

As the new guests sit, Imam Dabiri raises his hand. "I agree with my brother, Pastor Ravis. I propose that our committee go public with a 'minority opinion.' I know that this goes against the rules of the summit, but I think that the urgency of the crisis makes an exception in this case to be valid."

Looking at the nodding heads, Pastor Jones turns to Billy Lee. "Mr. Lee, would you be willing to act as spokesperson for us?"

"I would be honored to do so. However, I need to ask all of you to let my teacher speak. She has come a long way to talk with us."

The old woman stands again; she slowly bows to the group. "I am Aaradhya Sargretti, my great-grandmother was Kashvri Sargretti. I was born in what is now called New Delhi, India. My teacher sent me here to ask for your help."

"What kind of help?"

"We are working toward a new spiritual awakening in the world, and we see your committee as a group of allies in our work."

"Why haven't we heard of you?" asks one of the participants.

"Our organization avoids public scrutiny because we are a small group of people and because we had to wait until the current crisis began.

"I would like to share with you a dream I had that may help *us* all connect together. Then I want to hear about your dreams.

"I am walking at home in the morning, at Raj Ghat in New Delhi, which is our memorial to Mahatma Gandhi. A great stairway appears in the sky overhead, descending to a spot at my feet. An endless crowd of people assembles around me, praying and chanting. I look up to see a figure walking down slowly toward me. When she steps upon the earth and removes her scarf, I only then recognize her as me."

There is a quiet hush in the room. Billy Lee breaks the silence. "I had that dream." He looks around the room, and the others are starting to nod. "In my dream, I am sitting by the fire back home in the mountains. I am praying for wisdom from my ancestors. Then I see a figure coming toward me out of the trees. As he approaches, I can see his face in the light of the fire. It is my face."

Pastor Jones leans forward in her chair. "You know, I think I had a similar dream the other night as well. I had forgotten about it until now. I was standing in the main conference room, frustrated that the summit was not addressing the real issues confronting us today. Then I heard applause and saw a woman walking up to the front, preparing to address the summit. Excited that, finally, someone was going to lead us in a different direction, I joined in the applause. But when the woman turned around, I saw that it was me! I wonder what these dreams mean, and why we are all having them."

CHAPTER 18

A Visitor from the Sky

Key themes in scene:
1. A worldwide belief in extraterrestrials
2. Our hopes and fears about extraterrestrials are similar
to our hopes and fears about our goddesses and gods

Location: Hobyo (Obbia) Somalia
Date: July 5, 2050

She was perhaps the first human being to see the arrival of the being who was to be called the "SkyWoman."

Nasteeho Sagal is up very early. She is the 17-year-old daughter of a poor Somalian family that lives on the crowded shores of the Indian Sea, and it is her job to prepare the fishing nets before the boats go out. It is dark and overcast, but Nasteeho notices a sudden opening in the clouds where the stars can be seen on the edge of the galaxy.

It is then that she sees it. A soft indigo light apparently moving through the low clouds appears for a few moments and then disappears again at great speed.

"Praise Allah!" she says aloud. Nasteeho somehow knows that she has seen something important and runs up the beach to her house to tell her mother.

"Mother! I saw an angel!"

Location: Raj Ghat and the Shantivan, New Delhi, India
Date: July 5, 2050, a few minutes later

The first appearance of morning glow is barely visible as a lone figure walks quietly through the gardens, her hands clasped behind her.

Aadhya Amin is the lead curator of the gardens at Raj Ghat, the memorial for Mahatma Gandhi, and at the neighboring Shantivan, or "Garden of Peace," in New

Delhi, India. Every day, she arrives to work an hour early so she can do her walking meditation, expressing gratitude for the blessings she has been given. Aadhya grew up homeless in the slums of New Delhi. It was her lifelong fascination with and enthusiasm for plants that led her to pursue her work in gardening.

Looking down at the pathway, she notices that she can see the shadow of her body out in front of her. Turning around, she sees a light up in the sky, glowing a soft indigo color. She watches as it descends slowly until it is silently hovering over the open-air memorial to Mahatma Gandhi.

She falls to her knees and says a prayer as she is bathed in light. In a minute, she finds herself shaking. After clearing her mind, she picks up her phone and calls the director's office.

Location: Raj Ghat and the Shantivan, New Delhi, India
Date: July 5, 2050, three hours later

Already there are thousands of people in the park and the neighboring area. The object in the sky is now illuminated in the morning sun and appears to be a translucent and slightly pulsing ball of light, perhaps a dozen meters in diameter, of an indigo color. It hovers directly over the black marble Mahatma Gandhi memorial.

Someone called the police; they called the military; now Indian soldiers have been brought into the area. Several armored vehicles are parked nearby, each holding a traditional gold, red, and black flag that flaps in the morning breeze.

The news media are gathering just beyond the ring of military guards who have now formed a protective circle around the memorial area. Cameras are capturing images of the object, which are being sent around the world.

Location: Raj Ghat and the Shantivan, New Delhi, India
Date: July 5, 2050, that afternoon

Prime Minister Saanvi Anand arrives at the location that afternoon. Newly elected, she is very popular, particularly with the women of India who gave her strong support.

From the air, she stares, fascinated at the glowing object.

General Aarav Chabra meets her as she steps off her helicopter.

"Welcome, Prime Minister Anand."

"Thank you, General Chabra. Please update me on everything you know about our flying visitor."

"Unfortunately, we know very little, Prime Minister Anand. The object is partially solid since it reflects radar."

"Partially solid?"

"Yes, there seems to be a solid object inside some kind of energy field."

"What kind of solid object?" the prime minister asks.

"As best we can tell, it is a humanoid in shape and female. About 1.4 meters in length."

"Sounds like a young girl."

"Your guess is as good as ours."

Just then, the glowing object starts to descend slowly to the ground.

Some of the soldiers raise their weapons, and Prime Minister Anand immediately turns to the general.

"General, I want them to put away their weapons! If this being were hostile, she could have already harmed us."

"But there may be a danger—"

"That is an order, General. Absolutely no weapons. I take full responsibility."

As the object nears the ground, the field of energy dims and recedes until there is the figure of a woman standing on the ground, still glowing indigo. It is impossible to see her features. Only the outline of her body is visible inside the light.

The prime minister walks up to the figure, extending a hand. "Welcome, I am Prime Minister Anand of the Nation of India."

They take each other's hands.

As the being speaks, the words are not actually heard through the air, but inside everyone's heads.

"Thank you, Prime Minister. I have come here from my planet in peace and with a message for all of you. We know that Earth is in a time of crisis. We believe that we can help."

Drama and Psychedrama

CHAPTER 19

Drama

Key themes in scene:
1. Belief systems people have about the existence, power, and intentions of intelligent extraterrestrial beings
2. Hopes and fears people have when such beings appear

Location: Raj Ghat, New Delhi, India
Date: July 6, 2050

When you look up, the universe appears to be mostly empty space.

From the beginning of our time on Earth, we humans viewed the night sky and pondered our mostly empty universe with a mix of emotions. For perhaps as long, sightings of unidentified flying objects or UFOs have been seen filling these empty skies all over the world. Some believed that the early UFO reports were actually extraterrestrials whom our ancestors confused as gods and goddesses.

UFO reports intensified about a century ago in the 1950s as the first human space travel began. Although many thought that the reports were fiction, by 2050, an increasing majority of people in the world believe that extraterrestrials from space are regularly visiting Earth. This belief was supported by thousands of science fiction films, books, and documentaries that were eagerly consumed by people all over the world. After all these years of heightened anticipation about UFOs coming to Earth, humanity reacted with a mix of emotions as it learned that the day of a first visit had finally come.

Many are hopeful that the "SkyWoman" from space will help humanity with its problems. Many others are convinced that the last days have arrived and that the SkyWoman is here to warn humanity about its lack of faith in God and the coming apocalypse. Another large group is afraid that this alien being may have come to visit with some evil purpose.

An estimated nine billion people on the planet are watching live as Prime Minister Anand's simulacrum appears in homes, offices, and other locations across the world. She stands in front of the memorial at Raj Ghat.

"Namaste. Fellow people of Earth, I extend greetings to all of you from the people of India. As you know by now, we were contacted yesterday by a visitor from the sky who we are now calling the 'SkyWoman.' India is honored to have been chosen as the location for her visit and especially at the memorial of our beloved leader Mahatma Gandhi, which is a sacred place in our country.

"The SkyWoman has announced that she will be meeting with a group of representatives from Earth in about 48 hours from now at Raj Ghat, where she landed this morning. She is giving us a list of 21 participants whom she is inviting to this 'First Dialogue' meeting; it will be a diverse group of people who come from a variety of locations and cultures. Since only a few of the billions of people on Earth will actually be physically present, we will be streaming the dialogue to everyone. We will also create space for visitors who wish to come to New Delhi to sit nearby at the Shantivan, or Forest of Peace, which is also the cremation location of our revered first modern prime minister, Jawaharlal Nehru.

"I am convinced that the SkyWoman does come in peace, and I look forward, as I am sure we all do, to meeting with her." The prime minister's simulacrum fades away.

Location: Buenos Aries, the executive suite of GMU
Date: July 6, 2050

As Prime Minister Anand's image fades above them, for the first time that any of them remember, every man in the room is speechless.

Then, finally, a weak voice speaks up. "How do we know this is not some kind of marketing trick?"

"And a brilliant one at that!" someone responds.

There is nervous laughter.

GMU president Mr. Cheng raises his hand, and the participants in the conversation are quickly silent again, more out of fear than respect, although there is both.

"Gentlemen, we need to arrange a meeting with this SkyWoman. You all have heard the expression, that every man and … woman … has a price. Well, I can assure you that even our extraterrestrial visitor has a price!"

Mr. Cheng looks around the room with his intimidating dark eyes. He continues, "This is an opportunity of incredible importance for our organization. According to reports, SkyWoman has technology that generates a force field that completely protects her. She can also communicate through some kind of mental field. Just think about how she could bring us such new technologies that would keep us ahead of our competitors for the rest of the century!"

"Mr. Smythe and Mr. Brocktone, you are now my favorite intervention team after your success in securing the Mental Network for us on your recent trip to the university in Korea. You will go to India as soon as possible and arrange to be at this 'First Meeting.' Make contact with this SkyWoman and find out what her price is! I want to hear from you within the week."

As they walk out together, Mr. Smythe pulls Mr. Brocktone aside in the hall.

"Smythe," he whispers, "something tells me this trip is not such a good idea."

"You read my mind," Mr. Brocktone says in a snarky tone.

Location: Jakarta, Indonesia
Date: July 6, 2050

Current president of the Group of Thirteen and of Indonesia Mr. Kusumo convenes an emergency meeting of his fellow leaders via simulacrum from his "war room" in Jakarta.

"Welcome, everyone, and thank you for meeting at such short notice. Premier Petrov has informed me that his Foreign Intelligence Service has its preliminary assessment of the so-called SkyWoman. Premier Petrov?"

Petrov clears his throat and then proudly begins.

"Russia's intelligence services are the most advanced in the world, and we are happy to share our intelligence with you on this important and emerging story.

"Our assessment is that this is a real encounter with an extraterrestrial being from a civilization that is technologically much more advanced than ours. The so-called SkyWoman's technology enables her to hover in the air and to mask her body from being measured by our best military sensors. She is also is able to communicate with us through some kind of technology that links minds together. Apparently, she has indicated that she wishes to meet with a select group of human representatives at a meeting in New Delhi in two days.

"The Russian Republic will be inviting the SkyWoman to come to Moscow. India is still a backward nation, and Russia is much more suitable as the proper location of the first visit of an extraterrestrial race!"

President Browning from the United States raises her hand and is recognized.

"Thank you. I believe that Prime Minister Anand's simulacrum is now connected with us, and I want to hear from her. The United States recognizes the long and remarkable history of the nation of India, and we respect that nation as a suitable landing spot for the SkyWoman."

Premier Petrov frowns and sighs loudly, shaking his head. President Browning ignores him and continues.

"Prime Minister, what is your assessment, and what is your recommendation?"

"Thank you, President Browning. Yes, as you all know, I have just completed the announcement in our communications tent from the Raj Ghat site. I am convinced that the SkyWoman means us no harm and in fact has a gift for all of humanity. I have asked our army and our intelligence bureau to stand down all surveillance and weaponry, and to protect her from any uninvited outside interference.

"And as you know, she has asked me to organize a First Dialogue meeting with her and a select group of representatives from Earth. We are also preparing a large space at the nearby Shantivan Forest of Peace for visitors to sit."

"I want to be there!" interrupts President Çelik from Turkey. "Our country now has 94 million citizens, almost one-tenth of a billion, and we deserve a seat at the table."

"Mr. President, you are welcome to set up a tent in the Shantivan. Unfortunately, the SkyWoman has not yet given us a list of the twenty-one participants for the First Dialogue. We do expect to hear from her at any moment."

Location: Varanasi, India
Date: July 6, 2050

Although there are ancient Hindu stories of visits from deities from the skies, as there are in many other faith systems, this visit seems somehow different than all the rest.

Perhaps it is different mostly because it is actually happening, right now.

Everyone in the hall is waiting for King Chatterji to speak. As chief officiating priest at the Kashi Vishwanath Temple, the king has the responsibility to lead this emergency meeting. The king is a tall and imposing man with dark-brown skin and a kind disposition.

"Hello, everyone. A warm welcome to you all. We are all aware that the Sky-Woman has come to us at a troubled time. With 1.7 billion people, our country remains the most populated in the world. Although we have managed to feed ourselves, it has only been accomplished at a great price to our environment. And although India is a world leader in technology and especially space exploration, only a small fraction of our people gain direct benefits from our technological achievements. Two-thirds of our people live in cities, many in terrible poverty.

"We now have the historic opportunity to meet a visitor from the skies, as many of our ancestors did generations ago. Let us go to New Delhi and offer a warm welcome to our visitor!"

There is an enthusiastic response in the hall.

And inside of many hearts and minds, there is a mixture of excitement and fear. What would change in the next days and months? Perhaps everything.

Location: Mexico City, Mexico
Date: July 6, 2050

The people wanted something to cheer about. Now they believe they have it.

The country remains relatively poor, but proud. As Mexico's population grew to over 150,000,000 in 2050, inequalities in income and wealth also grew at an alarming rate. The impact of global warming is particularly felt here: soil moisture and water availability continue to worsen as the weather becomes hotter and drier. All attempts by the Green Party to reduce greenhouse emissions have been crushed by a government largely owned by corporate interests.

With almost 25 million people, Mexico City is now the tenth-largest city in the world. In downtown Mexico City, thousands of people are gathered at the historic Zocalo Plaza.

They watch the giant simulacrum of the Indian prime minister projected above them. As she finishes her public statement, the crowds burst into joyful celebration.

"Somos Salvos!"

"Somos Salvos!"

"We are saved!"

At the same time, about 80 km south of Mexico City in the small rural town of Tlayacapan, Morelos, the farmers watch the SkyWoman on their mobile phones. They leave their cucumber fields to meet at the local church. There they ask the priest to say a prayer.

Location: Rome, Italy
Date: July 6, 2050

Pope Luca sits with his Council of Cardinals in his Vatican chambers.

"Well, gentlemen, what do you think?"

All the men were intellectuals, and all were afraid. Cardinal Russo, Bishop of Rome, speaks. "Your Holiness, we believe that the SkyWoman is the Angel Gabriel sent to us by the Lord to prepare us for the coming last days of the apocalypse."

The pope jumps on the idea. "Yes, Bishop Russo. This is good. Would you please prepare a press release that serves to calm our people and that informs them that God has sent the holy Angel Gabriel back down to Earth to prepare us for the last days?"

Location: Omaha, Nebraska
Date: July 6, 2050

The Reverend Willy Shower sends a special message to his massive Internet following. He appears in his blue Sunday suit, sitting at his gigantic desk in his study. He announces solemnly that his evangelist Church of the Great Heartland has learned that the world will end in 30 days. Contributions to the church, he adds, are especially appreciated at a time like this and will also "help your status on the upcoming judgment day."

Calls are soon coming in with large donations and requests for prayer. Listeners begin to make their way toward the station, looking for shelter.

Location: Kandy, Sri Lanka
Date: July 6, 2050

At Sri Dalada Maligawa, or the Temple of the Sacred Tooth, the monks gather together to discuss how the community should respond to the SkyWoman.

Sister Kusum stands. "Sisters and brothers, thank you for gathering together so quickly. It is a lovely day today.

"We all know that we live in difficult times. Our small country is blessed with rich natural resources and rich historical traditions, but many of our people remain poor, and we have no powerful military to defend us.

"The visit from the SkyWoman may be a blessing. Or she may bring us more suffering. As our tradition teaches us, the future is impossible to know. I believe that the best response is for our community to send a small delegation to New Delhi to welcome our visitor. We know that most everyone wants to go, but with funds being limited, only three monks can be chosen. By lottery.

"Let us all send positive wishes and gratitude to our three representatives. With the gravity of the current crisis in the world, we will be meditating around the clock for the well-being of all beings."

Location: Queen Victoria Market, Melbourne, Australia
Date: July 6, 2050

Historically, Australia has been isolated from the other continents physically and psychologically. More and more, however, like all over the world, there is an underlying dis-ease in the country. Everyone knows that global and local conditions are gradually getting worse, but most people believe they are disempowered to do anything about it. In such conditions, there is a tendency to focus on one's own pleasures and distractions. The latest fast food and electronics keep most people sufficiently distracted and satiated.

Although Australia is blessed with many natural resources, including vast mineral wealth and beautiful beaches, all is not well with the economy. The country is one of a number of nations especially vulnerable to global warming. The people have watched the Great Barrier Reef slowly die over the past decades. At the same time, decades of drought have intensified the frequency and intensity of bush and forest fires and scorched the desert areas. The rise in sea level brought on by the melting of polar ice continues to affect the coastal regions where most people live.

Throughout and immediately after the broadcast from New Delhi, crowds began to gather in Queen Victoria Market. Melbourne's mix of people, primarily white people from the Anglican and Catholic communities, with a small number of darker-skinned Hindu People, are beginning to shout in unison, over and over.

"The SkyWoman has come to help us all!"

"The SkyWoman has come to save us all!"

"Praise to the SkyWoman."

On the sidewalk, a small group of Indigenous Australians watch the crowd. Leaning against the brick wall, they are dressed differently than the whites and Asians. Their hair is wild, like the land they love. They have seen the land and water they love slowly die. Making up only 3 percent of the population, they are still much more likely to be poor and unhealthy compared to the dominant racial and cultural groups. Their race and culture are slowly dying as well.

However, just like their fellow Australians shouting in the streets, they hope that the SkyWoman will help the world turn things around.

Location: Jerusalem, Israel
Date: July 6, 2050

In Jerusalem, both Imam Hussein and Rabbi Galante offer public statements that counsel their followers to stay at home, be calm, and pray. Despite their pleas, there is much unrest in the streets of the ancient city, and tension runs high between the different faith groups that live there. The Israeli Defense Force has been ordered to bring up two batteries of long-range acoustic devices for crowd control.

The two men happen to board the same high-speed geomagnetic train to Tel Aviv in preparation for boarding the next suborbital flight out of Ben Gurion International Airport to New Delhi.

As he walks to his seat, the imam recognizes the rabbi sitting in the coach section he is entering.

"Ah, Rabbi Galante, it appears that God has put us together on this train perhaps to go on a journey to India?"

The rabbi looks up and smiles at the imam. "Yes, I believe you are right, Imam Hussein." He looks around and notices that there are no other empty chairs. "Please. Please sit here and make yourself comfortable."

Unfortunately, the two men, having initially exchanged pleasantries, are actually nowhere near comfortable. Over the years, they have never met in person, despite the fact that they live in the same city. They have often found themselves on opposite sides of public controversies and have made unkind public comments about each other. Now thrown together on this journey, they both search for words to say.

CHAPTER 20

Invitations from the SkyWoman

Key themes in scene:
1. Range of reactions people might have when
contacted by an extraterrestrial
2. Fear people often have about being seen as insane when they
hear or see things that others do not seem to hear or see

Location: Salt Lake City
Date: July 7, 2050

Phil Parker is scared like he's never been before in his life.

He knew he had been under stress, but he was not prepared to for auditory hallucinations. The experience that he was having reminded him a little of the sensations he'd felt when using the advanced synthetic hallucinogens he took back when he was in college.

He was sitting at his home workstation when it happened. A woman's voice spoke in his head.

"Hello, Phil. Please do not be alarmed. I am the being they call the SkyWoman. I am contacting you to invite you to New Delhi. I want you to be a part of the Circle of 21 at the First Dialogue. I have arranged for you to be transported by your government."

Still at his desk, shaken and worried, Phil gets a phone call a few minutes later.

"Mr. Parker?"

"Yes?"

"This is Seetha Devi, chief of staff for Prime Minister Anand in India. The prime minister would be honored if you would be her guest at the first gathering with the SkyWoman in New Delhi. We have arranged with President Emily Browning for you to be flown from Hill Air Force Base on a military plane directly to New Delhi tonight. A military police escort will be in front of your house in a few minutes."

"What? Is this some kind of joke? Why me?" Phil asks.

"What I can tell you is that your name was identified in conversation with the SkyWoman herself."

At that moment, Phil hears the front door announce, "Guests are at the door for Phil."

He looks out the window and sees two sleek dark-blue military vehicles hovering out on the street in front of the house.

Location: Washington DC, the White House
Date: July 7, 2050

Steven Landing knew that the president had asked to not be disturbed. She was exhausted after the events of the last few days. Yet as her chief of staff, he knew that there was no question that he had to wake her.

President Emily Browning wakes to the buzzing sound of her "red phone," which was signaling an emergency. "Hello?"

"Madam President."

"Yes, Mr. Landing?"

"Seetha Devi, chief of staff for Prime Minister Anand in India just called to invite you to the First Meeting in New Delhi."

"Yes, I know," sighs the president.

"You know?"

"Yes, the SkyWoman just contacted me, apparently through her telepathic ability, and gave me a personal invitation. I will tell you more later. Please prepare a plane ... Oh and Steve?"

"Yes, Madam President?"

"Save a seat for the secretary of peace. Dr. Reeves will be invited as well. And there will be a third person traveling with us as well. A young man."

"Yes, ma'am."

A few minutes later, a visibly shaken secretary of peace walks into Steven Landing's office. He looks up at her and says, "Let me guess, Madam Secretary. You just received a telepathic message?"

"Uh, yes ... but ... how did you know?"

Location: San Francisco, California
Date: July 7, 2050

Some wanted to fire her immediately, others were afraid that public opinion would turn against them. Finally, late in the evening, they agreed to let her go in the morning, and they all went home and had sleepless nights.

Deanna Bradley got the notice of dismissal from GMU soon after she arrived at work. They called her into the office and told her that she would soon be hearing from their lawyers. Then they escorted her out of the office and onto the street where the protests had intensified after the interview the night before.

Someone recognized her, "Look, there's Deanna now!" They immediately surrounded her, and people were soon shaking her hand and thanking her for going public about the problems with the immortality treatments.

Not wanting any more publicity, she slipped away before the media people could corner her, disappearing down the stairs toward the BART station. On the train, she watched the TeleTouch news. The street violence had apparently become worse. Several protesters were killed in Chicago after police responded to reports of broken windows and burning cars in the Loop. Protests about the immortality treatments were also going on across the world.

It was when she arrived at home that it happened. She hears a voice in her head.

"Hello, Deanna. Please do not be alarmed. I am the being they call the SkyWoman. I am contacting you to invite you to New Delhi. I want you to be at the First Dialogue. I have arranged for you to be transported by your government."

Moments later, she got the call from Chief of Staff Seetha Devi with the offer of travel arrangements.

Location: Washington, DC
Date: July 7, 2050

Since he moved to DC, whenever he needed to reflect, Jean-Paul would sit at his favorite spot at the Reflecting Pool at the Lincoln Memorial.

So much had happened in the last few days. His best friend and adopted brother Dmytro had been killed, the Global One organization had exploded a nuclear device, the militaries of the world were mobilizing, he had met with the secretary of peace, and now the world had an extraterrestrial visitor. It is then that he too hears a voice.

"Hello, Jean-Paul. I am the being they call the SkyWoman. I am contacting you to invite you to New Delhi. I have arranged for you to be transported by your government."

Frightened at first that this is some kind of trick, Jean-Paul feels for the energy pistol he carries underneath his jacket. He notices a black government hovercraft approaching. Pulling out his weapon, he prepares to fight for his life.

The door opens on the craft and out steps Secretary of Peace Dr. Tasha Reeves. As he stands up, surprised, she smiles.

"Climb on in Jean-Paul and join the party. We are all going to India."

Location: Beijing, China
Date: July 7, 2050

As his plane ascends, Party Minister Yin looks out the window at Beijing's murky majesty. Despite limited government efforts to curb the air pollution, everyone could see and feel that it had become even worse over the past decade.

Why did Chairman Lau choose him to go to New Delhi? Yin knew that he probably irritated the chairman by asking questions at the meeting. But the chairman had reassured him that he also appreciated Yin's willingness and ability to think for himself, and that the mission to New Delhi would require critical thinking.

Much was now at stake. Hundreds of Chinese sailors had already died in the initial skirmishes in the Yellow Sea. There were now credible reports of massive military movements by Russia, Korea, Japan, and Indonesia. China was moving more forces of its own into the Yellow Sea, and some of the top generals were calling for a first strike.

Now this visit by the so-called SkyWoman had brought in a new unknown variable and further complicated an already chaotic situation. Yin wondered, as did many, about the timing of the visit. Did the extraterrestrials know about the crisis on earth? And if so, were they here to help humanity or perhaps to take advantage of its weaknesses and vulnerabilities?

Although he knows that he needs to sleep, he is wide awake and tense. As he leans back in his seat and closes his eyes, he hears a voice.

"Hello, Yin. Please do not be alarmed. I am contacting you to invite you to attend the First Dialogue. You will soon be contacted by the prime minister of India and informed that you are invited to the Council Tent."

Party Minister Yin smiles at himself. What an interesting dream; it must be the result of the new sleep medication that the doctor gave me, he thinks.

Just then, he feels a hand on his shoulder. It's his aide.

"Excuse me, Party Minister. So sorry to disturb you but we have just received a communication from India."

Location: Hainan, China
Date: July 7, 2050

There is a soft rain falling

Yu Yan Zhou lays next to her husband Bo, who lays on a bamboo mat on the grass outside of Haikou City People's Hospital. The hospital is full of patients and their families recovering from the explosion. Many have died, and many others have terrible burns, broken limbs, and other serious injuries. When they ran out of rooms, they had to start laying people outside on mats.

Bo had taken a bad fall when the bomb went off and was still unconscious, having suffered a concussion when his head hit a rock. Yu Yan is an herbalist in the local community and had always been leery of modern technology. She wants to take Bo home, but the doctors will not let her.

Physically and emotionally exhausted, she starts to fall asleep.

"Hello, Yu Yan. Please do not be alarmed. You will soon be contacted by the local authorities, and they will arrange to take you to Haikou Meilan International Airport. Do not worry about Bo; he is recovering now and will soon wake up. Your family will take good care of him, as I will watch over you on your visit here."

Yu Yan wakes up. Startled by the vividness of her dream about the SkyWoman, she looks over at her husband. His eyes are open, and he reaches out to take her hand.

"Yu Yan," he says, "yes, I heard the message too. She was in both our heads. You must go to India and make sure that the SkyWoman knows what happened here. It must not ever happen again!"

"I am so glad you are back, my husband," she responds.

Nodding, he smiles as he holds her hand.

Location: Tel Aviv, Israel
Date: July 7, 2050

Imam Hussein and Rabbi Galante are contacted by the SkyWoman as they sit on their suborbital plane lifting off from Ben Gurion International Airport.

"Hello, Imam Hussein and Rabbi Galante. Please do not be alarmed. I am the being they call the SkyWoman. I am contacting you to invite you both to be at the First Dialogue. You will be contacted by the government of India when you arrive in New Delhi and informed that you are invited to the Council Tent."

They look at each other with a mixture of amazement and awe.

Location: Nara, Japan
Date: July 7, 2050

Pastor Larah Jones, Billy Lee and Aaradhya Sargretti are also contacted at the same time as they meditate together in Todaiji in Nara, Japan.

The Japanese government responds immediately to a request from India to put all three of them on the fastest military plane to New Delhi.

Location: Suborbital space
Date: July 7, 2050

Mr. Smythe and Mr. Brocktone are contacted on their company plane as they enter suborbital flight.

"Hello, Mr. Smythe and Mr. Brocktone."

As they listen to the message from the SkyWoman, the two CEOs look at each other with a mixture of fear and excitement.

"Did you just hear something?" asks Smythe.

"Yes."

"Well, this may make our assignment much easier."

"Or perhaps more difficult," replies Brocktone. "Since this SkyWoman can enter our minds, she may also be able to read our minds."

"Yes, and in that case, our strategy would have to change."

Location: Korea and France
Date: July 7, 2050 (in Korea)

Dr. Jiu Kang, standing in front of her screens in her lab at Incheon National University, is testing the new mental communications technology with Dr. Adele Dubois at the University of Lorraine in Nancy, France.

"Jiu, our system seems to be functioning flawlessly, thanks to all of your hard work."

"And thanks to you and your team as well, Adele! Although, now I fear for our future. With control of our project passing to GMU, our invention may well become an instrument of the wealthy and privileged."

Just then, they both hear a voice.

"Hello, Dr. Kang and Dr. Dubois. Please do not be alarmed. I am the being they call the SkyWoman. I am contacting you to invite you both to be at the First Dialogue ..."

Location: Vladivostok, Russian Far East
Date: July 7, 2050

General Pomsky sits alone in his forward headquarters bunker hidden in the Russian Taiga Forest. He has just received a disturbing report that one of his robots was destroyed. The Chinese seem to have robots of their own now, with powerful directed energy weapons, and in an exchange of laser fire at the border, the Chinese robot had won. In light of these developments, the general decides to recommend to Moscow that the Russian Air Force deliver a surprise nuclear strike on China.

As he studies his maps, his concentration is interrupted by a voice that seems to be coming from inside his head.

"Hello, General Pomsky ..."

The general likes to think of himself as a rational man, and he offers a persona of logical thinking to everyone he encounters in his public interactions. However, when the SkyWoman invites him to India, this experience scares him. As he sits alone, he can feel his heart beating wildly. He has always been wary of being viewed as unstable because he knows that the government uses mental illness as an excuse for removing generals they are unhappy with. He does not want to spend the rest of his life in a psychiatric prison in Siberia.

Perhaps though, he thinks, the Chinese have found a way to mess with his head through some new super weapon they have developed.

This is the supreme moment of his career, and he cannot afford to lose it. He must pull himself together.

At that moment, the simulacrum of President Petrov appears in his bunker.

"General Pomsky?"

"Yes, yes, Mr. President?"

"Prepare yourself for a trip. You are going to New Delhi to represent our country!"

Location: Somalia
Date: July 7, 2050

Perhaps the most unique invitation came to Nasteeho Sagal in Somalia. Sitting on the beach with her mother, still thinking about the indigo-colored angel she saw the other night, she suddenly sees the light again! An indigo-colored sphere is descending toward them from the sky.

Both Nasteeho and her mother hear the voice at the same time.

"Hello, Duco Sagal and your beautiful daughter Nasteeho Sagal. Please do not be alarmed. I am the being they call the SkyWoman. I am contacting you, Nasteeho, to invite you to be my guest at the First Dialogue in India. Do not worry, Duco, I will watch your daughter. She is now seventeen, and she has wisdom beyond her age. I will transport her in the energy field that hovers above you."

Nasteeho turns to her mother. "Oh, mother, I want to go! I want to meet the SkyWoman. Perhaps she can help us!"

As her mother nods her approval, Nasteeho is surrounded by the indigo light and transported up into the African sky. The light is quickly flying back up into the clouds toward the east.

CHAPTER 21

A Refugee's Story

Key themes in scene:
1. Many refugees leave their homes because of intolerable conditions
2. They can bring their talents and abilities to their new homeland

Raj Ghat, New Delhi, India
Location: Raj Ghat and the Shantivan, New Delhi, India
Date: July 9, 2050

There are 22 chairs. One is left empty for the Sky Woman.

In the Circle of 21, as it came to be called, Prime Minister Saanvi Anand sits in the large tent with the other invitees chosen by the Sky Woman, all present for the first Council Meeting with the visitor from the sky. She sits next to the empty chair, and on her other side sits Aadhya Amin, the lead curator of the gardens at Raj Ghat and the second human to see the visitor. There is a hush in the room.

The curtain opens, and the visitor enters. She had been resting behind the curtain that divides the tent into two sections. She still glows in indigo light so that her features remain hidden and only her silhouette is visible.

She takes the empty chair next to the prime minister. Suddenly, everyone in the tent can hear her soft voice in their heads.

"Thank you for gathering with me this morning. I have a few things to say, and then you will have dialogue.

"When I arrived, I told you that I come in peace. My wish is that my visit with you will also help you all find a deep peace—a peace that is both within you and between you.

"I am a refugee in a sense, a refugee from a planet where an intelligent race is destroying itself and the beautiful planet they live on.

"We have been observing your planet for a long time.

"Consider your shared past. Imagine with me your planet inhabited for billions of years by plants and animals, all capable of creating offspring before they die. Every being lived as fully as possible on this beautiful planet before each surrendered to the inevitability of death.

"Although all these living things on Earth competed for resources, through strategies of both cooperation and violence, they did so in the spirit of their deep connectedness with everything else in their universe.

"Your human ancestors evolved an incredible awareness of their own awareness. This new mind was accompanied by the appearance of an ego in which each individual gained a sense of individuality and identification with mind but lost that spirit of connectedness with everything.

"Now in 2050, you have developed technologies that are capable of improving the quality and length of human life and certainly of ending it. You have developed weapons of mass destruction, and the recent detonation in China threatens to lead to a devastating nuclear robotic war. You also have developed technologies that enable you to communicate mentally across the planet, but these technologies are in danger of falling under the control of a powerful few. Your recent ability to freeze the aging process is still only available for a privileged few who are not spiritually prepared to live forever, and your race is still dangerously unprepared to become immortal. You also realize that your species has contributed to a dangerous process of climate change that is destroying the ecosystems that keep you all alive.

"Obviously, you have not yet learned to use these advanced material technologies wisely, and the existence of your species is at risk. Your species has mastered the material technologies of death and life, but it has not yet mastered the psycho-social-spiritual technologies that would enable humans to heal egocentrism, cooperate with and love each other, and use material technologies more wisely.

"It is possible for humankind to not only survive but also thrive. An important part of the process of mastering these psycho-social-spiritual technologies is the healing of the human ego. When we heal something, we make it 'whole,' The ego likes to hide from itself. The healing of the ego is about being conscious of the ego and seeing its activity in each moment.

"Every one of you has an ego, which is the tendency to identify. When I identify with something, the painful disconnection and accompanying aloneness I experience may be replaced for a moment with a sudden feeling of self-importance. I can identify with anything, including my body, my family, my possessions, my roles, and my beliefs. My beliefs about the world might include my religious and political opinions.

"Ego can also exist in a collective sense. A family can think of itself as superior to other families, just as a religious community can think of itself as superior to other religious communities. An entire nation, a race, or culture, for example, can also have a collective ego that compares itself with other groupings of people. Thus we can speak of the human Ego, with a capital 'E,' that is understood to be both individual and collective.

"I offer you two rituals that you can use to transform your lives. They are interdependent. The first is meditation, which is simply to see and accept the world the way it is. The second is dialogue, which is to respectfully listen for and speak the truth.

"Meditation can be done by one's self, in isolation, or collectively with other beings. Dialogue can also be internal, between one's own inner voices and between individuals, groups, people and other living things, and even people and the universe. These rituals are interdependent because they both involve consciousness. Consciousness is reverent awareness toward everything. Without consciousness, meditation and dialogue can become just expressions of Ego.

"One cannot have dialogue without seeing and accepting the world the way it is. And one cannot see and accept the world the way it is without the learning that comes from dialogic relationships.

"I come to first offer humanity three guided meditations, which are about three global outcomes that could occur. We will show you these potential futures because they all coexist right now. Humanity is at a crossroads, with three possible directions.

"With your help, I will offer these meditations to the human race. We might call them psychedrama meditations. A psychedrama is a spiritual story, a story of the development of the psyche's individual and collective consciousness.

"I am prepared to offer one meditation each day, over the next three days, to everyone in your world. The purpose of each psychedrama meditation is to see your world the way it is today and then to see a direction you could decide to move in.

"After the three psychedramas, you will be given an opportunity as a species to make a choice about the future you want. The three choices are essentially 'destruction,' 'survival,' or 'transformation.' If your race decides on destruction or survival, I will accept your decision and prepare to end my visit with you all. If you decide on transformation, I will stay to offer you a method of transformation, which we will call the Eternity Dialogues, in part because you will continue in dialogue forever.

"As you know, there is little time to lose. Your streets are in turmoil; your ecosystems are dying, and your militaries are preparing for imminent war. This evening, I will meet with all of you again to find out what the Circle of 21 would like to do. If you would like to do the three meditations, we will do our first global psychedrama together tomorrow. As you know, I am able to contact others telepathically. With your help, we will TeleTouch this telepathic experience across the world.

"I have selected those of you who sit with me in the circle as representatives of the human race. I will now retire to my side of the tent. You are all free to choose. I will not monitor your conversations, and you are all free to speak. I ask that your dialogue be facilitated by the female elder in your group, Aaradhya Sargretti.

"My question for your consideration today is, will you help me help you?"

CHAPTER 22

The Circle of 21

Key themes in scene:
1. When given a chance to participate in deep social change,
most people choose to participate
2. However, many different expectations and fears
will also often be activated in the process

Location: Raj Ghat, New Delhi, India
Date: July 10, 2050

In their awe-filled reaction to the SkyWoman's powerful presence, the attendees almost forget that most the people in the world are watching their simulacrums as they sit in the Circle of 21.

And as the SkyWoman leaves the room, there is a reverent silence.

The technicians activate the translation tools in the headsets that everyone wears in their right or left ear. In this way, everyone on Earth has access to instant transla-tion of what is being said into their own language.

Aaradhya Sargretti breaks the silence. "We are all here at the invitation of the Sky-Woman to decide whether we want to see the three possible futures of humanity. My friends, let us start our dialogue."

She pulls a stick, fashioned from a tree branch, out of her sling bag.

"I cut this stick from a Bodhi Tree, or Sacred Fig, which we also call the tree of enlightenment. In my homeland, it is a sacred tree. Many believe that the Buddha attained enlightenment when under such a tree. It is decorated with these rudrak-sha seeds, which we string as beads around the notch we make at the top of the stick. I always carry it with me.

"This will be our talking stick, which will help us take turns, respectfully shar-ing our own truths. We use the word 'little t' truth because we recognize that the perceptions of all of us are limited and that none of us have access to the totality of truth. We will pass it around the room, and only the person with the stick may speak. It is the speaker's responsibility to speak respectfully. It is everyone else's responsibility to listen for understanding. We will all help each other learn these rules, and we will be patient but firm when the rules are broken. We will pass the stick around the room, and those who wish to speak may do so when they receive it."

She hands the stick to Minister Yin, who is sitting next to her.

Party Minister Yin from China stands up.

"Thank you. The great state of China is interested in hearing what the Sky-Woman has to say. We welcome the meditations. We reserve the right, however, to not comply with any suggestions she may make or any agreements that may emerge from these dialogues."

Dr. Tasha Reeves, US secretary of peace, who is sitting next to the party minister, takes the stick. "Thank you. This stick is beautiful." She smiles. "Maybe I could borrow it for use in our often-dysfunctional political meetings back home," she says to Aaradhya Sargretti.

"I want to reaffirm the commitment that the United States has to developing a deep peace in this world, which is not only the absence of war but also a sustainable spirit of cooperation between and compassion for each other. I would also like to hear what the SkyWoman has to say. As a refugee from a planet that is incredibly advanced technologically but still in turmoil, she may have much to teach us."

Pastor Larah Jones from the World Religious Summit takes the stick next. "During my turn, I wish to say a prayer. May our visitor from space bring us the wisdom we all need now that will help us empower ourselves in these difficult times."

Sitting next to Larah is Phil Parker from Salt Lake City.

"It is an honor to be in this circle with all of you," he says. "I think about my husband and children at home. They are all frightened by the news we are hearing every day. I want them to live. I hope that we can work together, with the help of the SkyWoman, to turn things around on this planet for the good of our future generations."

The stick continues its journey around the table.

Yu Yan Zhou takes the stick into her hand, which is wrinkled with age and covered with spots from years of exposure to the sun. She smiles at Jean-Paul. "And I am one of the billions of aging people who also looks with equal dismay at what is happening. My husband and I were near the explosion in Hainan this week. He is still in the hospital recovering from a concussion. Many others were injured. Some died. It was terrible. I want my children and grandchildren to live in a world free from nuclear weapons and war robots. Let us work with the SkyWoman."

Imam Hussein smiles at Yu Yan as he takes the stick. "I am probably as old as you, my friend." He looks around the circle and gestures toward Rabbi Galante, who is sitting next to him. "My friends, I am ashamed. I am ashamed because

I consider myself a man of God, yet I have not taken the time to get to know Rabbi Galante, who lives and works only a few blocks from where I live and work in Jerusalem. Instead, I have had the bias that he is only a Jew and therefore an enemy of my people, the people of Islam. I have not seen until today how much I have been part of the problem of this world. Let us join hands today and work with the SkyWoman with the intent that we all learn to see our hidden biases about each other and recognize that all people on Earth are all truly the same people."

Rabbi Galante has a tear in his eye as he takes the stick. "The imam has spoken the words I would have said if the stick had come to me first. Thank you, my brother. My people, the Jewish people, have a long history of suffering, as you all know. But the imam is absolutely right. *All* people on this planet have participated as both perpetrators and victims of violence. We should add, we have also *all* been at times the observers of the violence, often complacent in our silence. Now is the time for us to stop being complacent observers of the violence that our race is perpetuating against not only each other but also against the ecosystems that support all life on Earth. Let us work with SkyWoman."

Next to receive the stick is Nasteeho Sagal. She is younger and smaller than the other 20 participants, but her presence is bright and clear.

"Hello. I am Nasteeho Sagal from Somalia. My mother is Duco Sagal. I too am honored to be here. I am told that I was blessed to be the first human being to see the SkyWoman coming down to visit us." She stops and looks around the room slowly. "There are many children around the world like me who were born into poverty. We can see what the wealthy have on our cell phones, but we discover that the opportunities and material things that are marketed to us through the web are really not meant for people like us. I am not complaining because I am happy. I expect someday to make a difference in my community. Like my sisters and brothers, I want the opportunity to live long enough to make a difference. We children of the world welcome the SkyWoman and ask for her help.

"I also want to share something else. I had a dream the night before I first saw the SkyWoman coming through the clouds. It was such a vivid dream that I told my mother about it. I feel that it is important to tell you all about it too.

"In the dream, I was looking up into the sky as I sat on the beach of the Great Sea in the dark of the new moon. The stars were brilliant and the wind increasing. I saw a brilliant indigo light up above me, descending slowly. I heard a voice in my head saying, 'I am here to help humanity.' I ran along the beach toward the place where the light touched the earth. As I got closer, I was surprised to see that the being in the light was in fact me.

"When I woke up, I told my mother about the dream. I asked her what it meant. She told me that it is a message from Great Spirit, telling me not only that each of us is responsible but also that *I* am responsible for the well-being of the earth and its people."

President Emily Browning takes the stick from Nasteeho Sagal. "My dear, *I* am honored to sit with you, a young woman so advanced in wisdom for your age. I agree with what you say about personal responsibility. I also see that there are billions of young people like you who have gifts to bring us all. In fact, it seems like only yesterday that I was your age, wishing that I could make a difference. I was given privileges in my life that gave me the opportunity to eventually become president of the United States. It is sad that it took so long for the United States to finally elect a female president. Perhaps you will be the first president of Somalia!

"My wish today is that we all unite across our differences of gender, race, religion, politics, age, and all the other differences that divide us. Let us work with SkyWoman and use her visit as an opportunity to do what we need to do to not only tackle the conditions of war, global warming, poverty, and disease that threaten our survival today but also to build toward a common future of cooperation and well-being."

Billy Lee from the World Religious Summit takes the stick next. "My name is Billy Lee. I am Oglala Lakota. My people live in the Pine Ridge district in what is called now South Dakota. I am also honored to be here and appreciate the leadership of President Browning, who has worked effectively for social justice for many minoritized people in what is now called the United States during her term.

"I support the SkyWoman. As a child, I was taught that the father of my people was Wanblee Galashka, a great eagle who came down from the sky and started a new race. Perhaps the SkyWoman will be the sky being who again starts a new race of people on Earth—a race of people who care for each other and for the planet."

President Kusumo from Indonesia clears his throat. The current president of the Group of Thirteen takes the stick in his hand. "I remember reading about a 'speaker's staff' when I was a young man in college in China, studying comparative religions, but I have to say, I have never used one until today. I like it though. I like how we are all taking turns as equals. Perhaps that is what we all need to learn: to treat each other with respect and as equals. Perhaps the SkyWoman can help us to do that; in fact, perhaps she is already teaching us about equality and mutual respect.

"I must add as the current president of the Group of Thirteen that I am dismayed by the abuse of power that I see as epidemic in our world. There has never been such an unequal distribution of power and wealth in the world as there is today. Most people see politicians as having vast power, and I am probably seen as the most powerful politician in the world by some. However, I have to tell you that we politicians are always living in fear. The more power that a person has in this world, the more that person is fearful of losing power. I am tired of living that way, of living in fear. Let us work with the SkyWoman and create a new world."

Sitting next to President Kusumo is Dr. Jiu Kang from Incheon National University in Korea. "I am thankful to have the opportunity to be here with all of you today. As a scientist, I try to look at things objectively, but I am also not without emotion. These events are remarkable, and I feel a great responsibility today. My scientific mind is curious. I want to see the SkyWoman's face and find out about her home planet. I want to find out how she found us here on Earth, a small planet in orbit around a normal boring yellow star. I want to know what went wrong on her home planet. I want to know *why* she wants to help us.

"I think we must cooperate with the SkyWoman. I agree with Party Minister Yin that we do not have to promise her anything yet. Let us listen to her stories and then hold a planetary dialogue and decide how to respond. As you all know, our university, along with our colleagues in France and elsewhere, has developed a Mental Web that can link us all together. Unfortunately, there are those who want to control our new technology.

"Most importantly, we now have an opportunity as human beings to talk about our shared future. Let's take that opportunity."

Mr. Smythe, one of the CEOs at GMU, takes the stick next. "Good day, everyone. Global Multinationals Unlimited is proud to be here at this first meeting with the SkyWoman. We would like to welcome the SkyWoman to Earth, and in recognition of this historic event, we would like to host her in a beautiful and secluded residence on one of our properties in the Andaman Islands off the coast of India in the Bay of Bengal. There would be space for all of you as well, of course, in our beach houses located on one of the adjacent properties."

He hands the stick to his colleague, Mr. Brocktone. "Yes, everyone, I join Mr. Smythe in welcoming the SkyWoman."

He pulls out a T-shirt from his pack, and he opens it up to show everyone. It has a drawing of the SkyWoman floating in the air. The following words are printed below it: "SKYWOMAN EVENT, NEW DELHI, 2050." On the back are the initials of GMU printed in red.

"This is a commemorative T-shirt that our subsidiary in New Delhi was able to design for this event. We have one for each of you, complimentary of GMU of course. And GMU is happy to work with the SkyWoman."

Dr. Adele Dubois from the University of Lorraine in Nancy, France, is sitting next to Mr. Brocktone. "I am honored to be here today. On behalf of my colleagues at the university, as well as on behalf of all of the citizens of the European Union, I want to welcome the SkyWoman. It is our fervent hope that her visit to Earth will lead to not only a deep world peace but also to the enhanced well-being of everyone who lives on our planet. We look forward to hearing from the SkyWoman."

General Pomsky of the Russian Army takes the talking stick in his suntanned hand. Sweating from the heat, he wears the heavy camouflaged uniform of the Eastern Command with the stars of his rank on his chest. "Ladies and gentlemen.

I am from Vladivostok and spend my time in Eastern Siberia, which is quite a bit north of here, and I am afraid I am not quite yet used to your climate. However, I have never been to New Delhi, and I must say it is beautiful.

"The Russian people are happy to welcome the SkyWoman. Our country is the largest, by area, in the world, with eleven time zones and vast areas of Europe and Asia. Within our borders live people from over one hundred and sixty ethnicities. We, therefore, represent a good percentage of humanity.

"We welcome the presentations that the SkyWoman wants to offer humanity. However, like the People of China, we reserve the right to make independent decisions about how we want to cooperate, if at all, with the SkyWoman. Our government also extends an official invitation to the SkyWoman to visit Moscow, our great capital."

Jean-Paul the young man from Global One, takes the stick in his hand. "Hello, everyone. I am Jean-Paul from Colombia. I belong to what most of you would call a terrorist organization. When I was a child, my family was taken away by government soldiers, and murdered.

"A few days ago, my adopted brother was also murdered, again by soldiers. I thought I was going to be killed as well. There are probably some of you in the circle today who want me killed and my organization destroyed.

"Yes, I was coleader of Global One from the beginning." He looks at Yu Yan Zhou and speaks to her. "Yu Yan, I opposed the use of the bomb in China, and that is why they took away my leadership. I deeply apologize to you and to your people. I hope your husband recovers fully from his injuries.

"I have no idea why the SkyWoman invited me here. In fact, I wonder how she even knew that I exist. However, I am still alive, and I am here in New Delhi with all of you.

"I say, let's listen to what she has to say. Our world needs all the help it can get."

Aadhya Amin, the lead curator of the gardens at Raj Ghat, holds the stick. "I am Aadhya. My parents were also poor, like yours" he says, looking at Jean-Paul. "I take care of these gardens for the people of India, and in the memory of Mahatma Gandhi and Prime Minister Nehru. I am honored to be able to speak with all of you today. I also want to listen to what the SkyWoman wants to say."

Prime Minister Saanvi Anand takes the talking stick. "What an honor it is to be here with all of you, and to represent the people of Earth in conversation with the SkyWoman. I have had a sense of calmness and presence since I arrived here to meet her. It is my fervent wish that her visit leads to similar positive change for everyone in our world. Let us cooperate together, like sisters and brothers, in the coming days."

The stick comes around to Deanna Bradley, the social worker from San Francisco. She also has a tear in her eye. "My hope is that the SkyWoman can help us use our technologies for good. Our new-found ability to create immortality seems to be killing us. On a global level, we are all armed and ready to murder each other.

We are even fighting over our newfound ability to communicate with each other. I too hope for change, before it is too late."

Finally, the stick returns to its owner.

"I am Aaradhya Sargretti. My great-grandmother was Kashvri Sargretti. I was born here in New Delhi many years ago. I belong to a group of women who call themselves the Great-Grandmothers or the Elephant Clan. We wear the image of the elephant because the elephant race is similar to the human race in that the females often live far beyond the time of menopause. This extension of life is necessary so that the older women can help lead the tribe through their acquired wisdom. The Great-Grandmothers meet to do spiritual practices for the purpose of supporting the highest good for our planet. I too am honored to be here and to have the privilege to facilitate this dialogue in the Circle of 21."

Location: Raj Ghat, New Delhi, India
Date: July 10, 2050

The SkyWoman returns to circle that evening.

When everyone is seated, Aaradhya Sargretti stands before the circle and all of humanity.

"The circle has decided unanimously to participate in your three psychedramas. Then we may want to meet with you again about the dialogues you proposed."

"Very good. Thank you. I will see you all tomorrow."

CHAPTER 23

First Psychedrama: Ego and Destruction

Key themes in scene:
1. Ego is related to identification, especially identification with belief
2. Such identification as belief in the superiority of a particular
nation, ethnicity, culture, or religion can lead to violence because
identification allows the person to silence and dehumanize the Other

Location: Raj Ghat, New Delhi, India
Date: July 11, 2050

The moment is finally here.

Dr. Jiu Kang and her colleagues have set up a Mental Amplifier in the room. The SkyWoman asked for the equipment, explaining that the amplifier would allow her to directly access the new Mental Web using the satellite systems recently launched from the salt flats in the Utah desert.

Most world leaders made every effort to encourage people to access the Mental Web. Instructions on how and when to tune in were distributed. To protect each person's privacy, Dr. Kang and her team had developed a simple system of thoughts and hand motions that would open up the energy field for people to join in or leave the Mental Web. People who were unable to make the hand gestures, such as the disabled, were given alternatives. Very young children and infants were unable to participate fully in the system, but in many cases, their parents helped set them up.

There was, of course, some resistance, particularly from some religious leaders who told their followers that the SkyWoman was a "false prophet" or "agent of evil." Still, well over nine billion people were participating, which has never happened before in history.

Now, all over the world, people are preparing for the event.

In Hainan, China, Bo, the husband of Yu Yan Zhou, lays on his cot outside Haikou City People's Hospital. Like the other patients around him, he is waiting to join in the meditation. He is proud that his wife is one of the Circle of 21, and he has told everyone in the hospital about it, some of them multiple times.

In Hobyo, Somalia, Duco Sagal, the mother of Nasteeho Sagal, sits in her small hut with her other four children as they wait for the meditation. She too is so proud of her daughter, and everything that has happened in the past few days seems like a dream.

In Salt Lake City, Sid and his three children, Matti, Benton, and Frederick, sit together at home watching the simulacrum of the scene in New Delhi. They are also proud that Phil was chosen to be one of the 21 participants. The world seems so different than it was a few days ago.

In Loiyangalani on Lake Turkana, in the Great Rift Valley of Kenya, a small group of older women also preparing for the meditation. The Great-Grandmothers are proud that Aaradhya Sargretti was chosen to lead the 21 Participants. Perhaps she can make a difference. Much is at stake.

In New Delhi, the SkyWoman, blazing in indigo, joins the circle. The 21 participants in the circle are sitting in their chairs, ready. Then the now-familiar voice speaks in their heads.

"Hello to all of the participants in this circle here in New Delhi, India, and to everyone in the great Earth sphere. I am the being you call the SkyWoman. Thanks to all of you who are participating and especially to those of you willing to stay awake to participate. This week, we will alternate times for the three meditation events so that we all take turns participating during our intervals of day and night.

"I am going to take you on a guided journey to one of three possible futures that exist in front of humanity. Our intent is to see this future together so that you can consider these choices and dialogue about what you want and what you do not want.

"You will all be hearing my words in your heads, and you will also see, hear, taste, touch, and feel some of the experiences I will share with you. During this journey today, you will not have an opportunity to respond. That opportunity will come a little later in our process.

"Please, everyone, find a comfortable location to sit or lie down and then close your eyes. For some parts of the meditation, I will speak as if I am you. And now I will first notice my thoughts. I may not have been as aware of my thoughts before this moment because I was busy or distracted. I will look at my thoughts like I look at clouds in the sky, watching them float past, always changing, always moving across the horizon of my consciousness and then disappearing, only to be replaced by other thoughts. Now, I will recognize my body, noticing how it may be tense in places, in pain in places, at ease in places. I am watching my body sensations as they may move across my awareness, like clouds in the sky. And I may also feel Spirit in whatever way I may understand Spirit and am able to feel It. Perhaps I feel Spirit as a body sensation. Perhaps It is in an image. Perhaps something else.

"Now I can open my body, mind, and spirit to share in an experience that most other people on Earth will be having at the same time. The SkyWoman will be showing

me thoughts and sensory images in a story she is telling. In a few moments, I will start to see a kind of virtual reality experience in my mind. The experience will have sound and color and other sensations. It may at times become uncomfortable, but I can let my reactions flow through me like water through a wild river canyon.

"I am doing this work for the highest good of myself, and for all the beings on this planet. I will receive loving comfort and support when I experience difficult thoughts or emotions."

At this moment, the billions of people in the world who are participating with SkyWoman all see a representation of the universe. There is a vast panorama of energy pulsating in gigantic ripples of light and darkness. The pattern looks like the many waves on a still pond after a stone falls through the surface, and only the waves move more gradually and in three dimensions.

"I can see our universe. All things in the universe, including all beings, emit energy. I can experience the energy of the universe bathing everything with its vitality. Perhaps I can see this energy. Perhaps I can feel the energy."

Then everyone sees a galaxy in space.

"I can see how my own galaxy looks, from the Andromeda Galaxy, your closest galactic neighbor, from 2.5 million light years away. Light goes 9.5 trillion kilometers in one year. That is a distance in kilometers of two thousand three hundred and seventy-five followed by sixteen more zeroes. I can see the energy of the galaxy emanating into the universe. I can see the energy of the galaxy moving out into space."

Then everyone sees a sky full of stars.

"I can see what my local sun looks like from the nearest star, Proxima Centauri, 4.24 light years away. That is about forty trillion kilometers away. The yellow star in the middle is our sun. I can feel the energy of the sun."

Then everyone sees planet Earth from out in space. It is a beautiful green, blue, red, white, and orange sphere.

"This is what my home planet looks like from space, from about 384,400 kilometers away, the average distance of your moon. I can experience the interacting energies of the moon and Earth."

A solar eclipse comes into view.

"Now I see a solar eclipse viewed from Earth. The moon is passing between Earth and the sun, casting a shadow on Earth. The solar eclipse is an awesome and beautiful thing on any planet. In my tradition, on my home planet, the eclipse is about letting go. The sun is gone for a few minutes, and we reflect on what we need to let go of to heal ourselves, our communities, and our planet."

Then each person sees his or her own body.

"This is what I look like from another person's perspective, who may be standing two meters away from me. I can see my own energy emanating from my body."

Then each person sees a body lit up like a field of energy. There are waves of energy entering and leaving the body, interacting with everything else.

"This is what the energy looks like when it is allowed to move out from and into my body. It looks similar to the pulsating waves of energy in the universe I saw earlier. It moves in and out of the body. I may see many colors of various intensities and hues. The energy connects my body with other people and with everything else in the universe."

The pictures changes.

"If I look carefully, I can now see a silhouette of my body that eclipses my body's light, much like the moon can act as a backlit silhouette that masks much of the sun's light during a solar eclipse. This is how my ego looks from an energetic standpoint; it blocks the natural energetic connection.

"The ego is the sense of 'me,' the sense of a separate identity that every human has. The ego identifies with different forms, such as the body, the tribe, or the beliefs I may have. In ancient times, people with the strongest egos might have had a material advantage over others since a strong ego enables people to individually and collectively use resources without restraint and even treat other humans as resources, using and killing them when the ego thinks that is necessary.

"I can see how much of the energy from my body is eclipsed by my ego and how much my ego stops the energy of the universe from interacting with my body. If I do not learn to heal my ego, then I will have a permanent eclipse of the inner light of my being."

Now each person looks at his or her own family and local community. There is the energy of all these beings moving and swirling about in space. Whether it is a city with millions of people or a tiny village, the energies of people, other animals, and plants swirl and mix together, with the earth.

"I can now see how the energy of my family and community naturally interacts with Creation."

The picture changes. And the whole earth seems alive with energy, interacting with space.

"Now I can also see visually how the collective ego of my family and community currently separates our energy from interacting with other people and with the earth."

As the SkyWoman speaks, people see the collective energy of their neighborhoods, villages, farms, or cities become eclipsed for a few moments. Their communities are separated from other communities and from the earth by the eclipse.

Then the energy display ends, and everyone sees Earth from about 160 km above the earth. Everyone is looking directly down on the South China Sea.

"Now, sisters and brothers, let us look together at what will happen if you allow the individual and collective ego of humanity rule the world. The illusion of separateness will lead to destruction; it always does. This will be painful to view, but we must do this to heal. Healing makes us whole; healing is seeing the whole thing, seeing the universe and ourselves exactly as things really are. Hate and violence are only possible when you believe you are separate from the Other."

Then the people of Earth watch what is going on in the South China Sea. War robots from many nations are cruising about on the water, under the water, above the water, and even way up in space orbit. The energy fields of most of the soldiers and sailors, and of most of their field commanders are eclipsed by ego, as they identify with the nationalities they belong to and become blind to the connections they have with people from other countries.

Then the people watch as they see the corporate, political, religious, and military leaders who are controlling the armies and navies. Most of these leaders also have energy fields eclipsed by their egos.

But it is not just the leaders who are responsible.

Now the people see how everyone is responsible. The people watch how the energy fields of most humans on Earth are eclipsed by ego. They observe how ego allows a person to forget about the connection of all things and instead hate other people. They observe that war would not be possible without ego.

"And now I see that the war robots are unleashed."

The people watch as the South China Sea explodes. Thousands of sailors die in the first minutes as they are vaporized by nuclear weapons and high-energy beams. Many planes, ships, and satellites of many navies disappear in fire and smoke.

Then the conflict widens like a fast-moving fire in dry, windy brush. The people watch political and military leaders around the world react in their ego-fed fear.

No one knew how many bombs and robots had been manufactured, because many nations, some large and some quite small, had secretly built or purchased such weapons over the years.

Robot armies are launched on land, in the sea, and in the air. The robots murder millions of people. Thousands of missiles are fired from satellites down to their targets on the ground. Perhaps 200,000 nuclear weapons are detonated, and billions immediately die.

Cities disappear in fire and smoke. Many other living things, including wildlife, forests, and grasslands, are killed as well. Most of the ecosystems that support life are poisoned.

There is no continent, no country on Earth that is not in flames.

Most of the people watch their loved ones die. They witness their own deaths.

"Now, sisters and brothers, there is more to see. Let us visit your Earth 25 years after the war, about a generation from now when your children will have become adults."

The people see a planetary ecosystem still in deep shock. Nuclear winter remains a reality, with cool weather still persisting all across the planet. Radiation, lack of sunlight, and colder temperatures have colluded to kill most of the plants and animals that humans used for food. After a quarter century, food stockpiles have all been emptied.

Some people's children did survive the war. Some people watch as they see their own child or other children struggling. They see the survivors starving and suffering from disease and exposure, living in a still-blackened world.

The farthest northern and southern latitudes remain cold and uninhabited. Most of the people who survived the initial explosions have died from starvation, war, and disease. Those who are still alive primarily exist in rural, subtropical regions, and most of them suffer from nuclear famine, disease, anxiety, and depression.

"And now, let us look together at the earth in about two generations, 50 years from now, in the times of our grandchildren's lives."

Now the people of Earth see scenes that are even bleaker and more disturbing. Even after 50 years, recovery from the destruction of World War III has barely begun.

The ecosystems that support life remain in tremendous disequilibrium. Pockets of high radiation exist in every region of the planet. Although some forests and animal populations have recuperated, most living things are still poisoned by radiation and other toxins. Even the oceans have become almost empty of life.

Most of the former human world order has been destroyed and in its place are a few isolated settlements that all struggle to survive.

For most people participating in the psychodrama meditation, they have no direct descendants living anymore. Those who do see their grandchildren suffering from hunger, exposure, disease, isolation, and despair.

Even the wealthy and powerful who were initially able to shield themselves and their own families from the disaster by retreating to bomb shelters are dead. Most eventually died from hunger and disease. Some were killed by other people who discovered that they were hoarding the last food stores.

"Finally, let us look at about three generations of time after the great war, which you would call World War III. As we will see, in 75 years, all human life is gone.

"In this last scene in the meditation, the earth is now slowly repopulating with animal and plant species. As was the case in other mass extinctions in Earth's history, some species do well but many others die off completely. One of the many species that now is extinct is the Hominidae, which includes such 'great apes' as gorillas, chimpanzees, and humans. It turned out that Homo sapiens is a species especially vulnerable to the short- and long-term effects of radiation poisoning."

The people see that the skeletons of the cities and towns and connecting infrastructures across the world are slowly deteriorating. Where there were once paved roads and parking lots, a variety of plant life is growing through the widening cracks. Even the biggest structures in the great cities are slowly crumbling, although vestiges of steel and concrete will last thousands, even millions, of years. The bones of billions of humans are gradually deteriorating as well, although some will become fossilized, perhaps for some future intelligent race to discover.

"Now, my fellow travelers, you are free to begin experimenting with your first global dialogue. I am using my own abilities to support the technology of your new Mental Web so you can speak with each other and with me.

"Those who choose to participate will notice that, although it is possible to mentally connect with particular individuals you may wish to engage with, it is also possible to connect with the large waves of emotions that wash across your species. In other words, you humans create both individual and collective energy fields that you can connect

with and use in your communications. These emotion-waves, which have not yet been detected by your scientists but which have been sensed by the more spiritually developed among you, have always existed. Your Mental Web allows you to make these connections, and someday you will learn to communicate like this without physical technology. Indeed, someday you will learn that it is possible to communicate not only with your own species but also with all other living things."

Just like the SkyWoman said they would, every human who is listening suddenly has access to what seems to be an infinite number of communication channels. It is as if humans can now sense and join in the collective experiences that many thousands, millions, and even billions of humans share.

Some people wonder whether these individual and collective connections have always in fact been available to humanity, much like the long waves that cross the surfaces of the oceans. And if they always existed, why did they not see them, they wonder.

And other people think about the millions of people on the planet who have experienced what Western psychologists have for many decades called "psychotic hallucinations" and what many other cultures have called "visions" or "spiritual gifts." They now wonder if it is possible that at least some of those experiences were not so much the result of "mental illness" but rather a sensitivity that had perhaps once been understood by earlier cultures and then forgotten.

In fact, many things suddenly look different to many people on the planet. Is that because the SkyWoman has opened their eyes to reality, they wonder, or has she simply fed them new lies?

CHAPTER 24

Second Psychedrama:
Tolerance and Survival

Key themes in scene:
*1. Most people want to survive, and people may be able to continue
surviving without doing the difficult work of healing the ego*
*2. Tolerance may be preferable to overt violence, but mere tolerance of the
status quo is unlikely to lead to the kinds of transformations necessary
for the long-term well-being of humanity and is more likely to lead to
a condition of global survival with steadily decreasing environmental
conditions and a worsening of overall conditions for humanity*

Location: Raj Ghat, New Delhi, India
Date: July 12, 2050

All around the world, people notice that something has changed.

When folks pass each other in their homes, on the street, or out in the fields, they exchange a knowing glance. Perhaps it is the recognition that most everyone has shared in a similar experience, perhaps for the first time, in human history.

Perhaps it is also the shared sense of the beautiful world that humans still have and of how close everyone is to losing it all.

All over the world, people are preparing for the second psychedrama meditation.

In Hainan, China, Bo Zhou is now strong enough to sit up. He sits in the lotus position on the mat he slept on last night and waits for the SkyWoman to start to communicate. He is still surrounded by a hundred or more other people who also could not be accommodated inside the hospital. Three more of the victims from the nuclear explosion died last night, and they just collected the bodies and took them away a few minutes ago.

In Hobyo, Somalia, Duco Sagal calls her children to enter the hut. The dogs are barking and Duco looks out to see her neighbors walking up the road to join them. She waves to them.

"Hurry now, the SkyWoman will be talking in a few minutes."

In Salt Lake City, Sid, Matti, Benton, and Frederick sit together on the porch, looking at the smoke blowing into the valley from the latest fires in California. Every summer, it seems the fires get worse throughout the western states, as the current 20-year drought continues. The smoke reminds them of the smoke in yesterday's meditation.

In Loiyangalani on Lake Turkana, Kenya, the Great-Grandmothers watch the cormorants and flamingos from the lake shore. It has been very dry here, too, in Eastern Africa; climate change continues to accelerate, creating unfamiliar weather extremes across the globe. The wind kicks up dusty whirlwinds that lift the parched soil hundreds of feet in the air. Sitting down now in a circle, the Great-Grandmothers also wait for the SkyWoman to join them.

In New Delhi, the SkyWoman joins the 21 participants in the circle.

"Hello to all of the participants in this circle here in New Delhi, India, and to everyone in the great Earth sphere. Yesterday, we explored what will happen if humanity continues to think and behave in the same way it has for thousands of years. Today, we will do the second psychedrama meditation, which we will call 'tolerance and survival.' In this meditation, we will look at what will happen if humanity is willing to tolerate each other just enough to survive as a species, which is what you have been doing for many years. It will be up to all of you, of course, to decide whether 'just enough to survive' is actually good enough for you and your descendants.

"Please, everyone, find a comfortable location to sit or lie down and then close your eyes. I will again sometimes speak as if I am you. Each of us will watch our mind and body as I taught you to do yesterday."

The SkyWoman takes everyone through a beginning meditation about the body and mind, similar to what she did the day before. The she continues.

"Now I can open my body, mind, and spirit to share in an experience that most other people on Earth will be having at the same time. The SkyWoman will be showing me thoughts and sensory images in a story she is telling. Some of the experiences in the story may be disturbing; some may feel good."

Each of the nine billion people on the planet who are participating in this meditation now see the earth from space. They can see the energy of the earth flowing inside and through the planet. And now they see the most powerful people on the planet. Most are focused on maintaining and expanding their power and control. In almost every case, their energy is still eclipsed by their individual ego. And now they see other people on the planet who have tempered and even healed their egos. Many of them are making positive differences in their families and communities.

Then they see the Yellow Sea, where the armed conflict has begun. People are dying. Most of the existing political institutions are ineffective in stopping the conflict. Although most of the politicians who lead the most powerful countries realize that no one wins a nuclear war, they also are under tremendous pressure from their military leaders and other more conservative elements in their countries to take a tough posture. Therefore, the news is full of threats and counter-threats from the different nations. Some leaders have already made arrangements to go to their secret bomb shelters.

The United Nations rushes to convene a conference, but as usual, the most powerful nations keep the discussion in a deadlock of mutual blaming. Instead, those powerful nations veto all proposals to end the conflicts in a just and peaceful way.

The CEOs realize that a devastated world will not be a profitable world. They have also built secret bomb shelters, just in case things go bad. Ultimately, they put pressure on the political leaders to contain the violence to the Yellow Sea. Enough of the weapons that they have sold to the militaries of the world have been tested and destroyed that they can now make huge profits in replacing them and upgrading militaries to a new generation of destructive technologies.

The religious leaders approach the crisis in different ways. Some preach that the last days are coming. Others ask their followers to be calm and nonreactive. Some call for military strikes against their "enemies."

The revolutionaries are blamed by many for the crisis. Most of them are arrested by police forces. Some are tortured in their cells.

Most of the politicians bow to the influence of the CEOs, and their militaries are told to stand down.

World War III is narrowly averted. Again.

The SkyWoman speaks.

"Now, my children, there is more to see. Like we did yesterday, let us visit your Earth 25 years after the war, about a generation from now, when your children become adults."

The meditation moves to a view of the future. The people see a world in 2075 that is much like it was in 2050. Most of the wealth and power in the world is still controlled by a privileged few. In fact, the balance of wealth and power are even more concentrated in the hands of the few.

The people who are parents see the lives of their children.

In 2075, over a billion children live in poverty, and hundreds of millions of them are dying from hunger and preventable diseases. Billions of people who belong to minoritized populations are living in substandard housing, many without clean water to drink and clean air to breathe.

The middle and wealthy classes also continue to suffer from epidemic levels of substance abuse, depression, anxiety, and suicide, all associated with the gradual and steady increase in climate change, overpopulation, species extinction, environmental pollution, and environmental diseases associated with toxins, radiation, chemicals, and deteriorating ecosystems.

There are still "small wars" going on, mostly in the poorer regions in the world. Many of these are "proxy" wars between the great powers who pour military weapons into smaller countries to assist their favorite combatants. The corporations also seek to test their new weapons in these wars. Many people are killed or maimed in the conflicts. Most of these are civilians. Millions more are displaced refugees with nowhere to go. Wealthier nations are reluctant to accept these refugees, and clever politicians use that reluctance to gain power, so the refugees tend to move to other poor nations in increasingly vast camps populated with poverty, disease, and crime.

Technological progress, in the material realms, continues to accelerate.

The corporations own the World Mental Web and every person's thoughts and behaviors are increasingly under surveillance for their entire lives. When people are born, they have a permanent chip implanted into their heads that connects them with every other person and with corporate and government computers. If people try to have their chips removed, they are subject to severe penalties and even imprisonment. Attempts to introduce viruses into the network are immediately met with harsh responses by police who can now track all technologically assisted communications.

The corporations also continue to own the immortality treatments. Despite promises to make the treatments affordable, this has not happened. A few token "scholarships" are offered online through their marketing and public relations offices. In addition, most people who get the treatments still struggle with psychological and spiritual distress. These struggles are viewed as "psychological disorders" by the medical elite and largely treated with medications. About 15 million people now are in various stages of "immortality." Studies show that they are, as a whole, actually less happy than the general population. These studies are suppressed.

Resentment toward the wealthy is epidemic, and many wealthy people increasingly have migrated to "gated communities" that are protected by sensors and well-armed robots. The wealthiest have also purchased robots that serve as their armed guards. These machines protect their human masters from kidnapping and robbery attempts when they venture out from their gated communities.

The militaries of the world have become even better armed than they were in 2050. Tiny robots are now manufactured by the corporations that can seek out and kill individuals who are targeted for elimination. Some robots are designed to pass as insects, which are increasingly used to assassinate perceived enemies by governments and other corporate interests. Thousands of nuclear weapons are now in orbit around the earth, poised for launch.

A new wave of revolutionaries has emerged. Many of them use terror tactics, and some of their tactics include mass-casualty attacks. These attacks occur on almost a daily occurrence somewhere in the world.

"Let us visit your Earth 50 years after the Battle of the South China Sea, about two generations from now, when your grandchildren will become adults."

The people see a world that has slipped even further into disconnection and despair. Those who already have grandchildren now see them as adults. The problems that existed in 2075 are all a little worse in 2100.

World population is now close to 13 billion. About two-thirds of the population live in cities, and many of these are megacities. With the highest fertility rates now in sub-Saharan Africa and Southeast Asia, and with slight increases in life expectancy in these poorer countries, many now live in desperately crowded urban conditions full of alienated youth and aging populations with little purpose in life besides survival.

In fact, survival is the theme of mankind. Urban life is also difficult in the wealthiest countries, as continued inequality across race, ethnicity, and social class has led to increasing tensions, segregation, and crime. As national parks and monuments become increasingly under attack by corporations seeking to extract the remaining minerals and energy resources in the earth, most people have little if any exposure to wild lands. Climate change and environmental deterioration continue to accelerate; microplastics are now in all the oceans and freshwater on Earth and the seas are slowly drowning the great coastal cities. The few remaining wild lands are being loved to death by crowds of people seeking to satisfy their need for ecophilia, or connection with nature.

So-called mental illness continues to be recognized as the leading world health problem, with increasing numbers of people of all ages struggling with physical and mental symptoms that the health care systems do not understand. In the overdeveloped nations, mental health treatments usually involve potent mixtures of psychotropic medications and so-called cognitive therapies. In the underdeveloped nations, symptoms are still viewed as signs of potential spiritual gifts, and people with these symptoms are more likely to be accepted and integrated into their communities.

"And, finally, let us visit your Earth 75 years from now, or about three generations into the future, when your great-grandchildren will be adults."

In 2125, the same patterns on earth, seen in 2075 and 2100, continue. Population, inequality, poverty, violence, and illness increase even as the global ecosystem continues to deteriorate.

More and more nations are participating in space travel. Attention is focused on building systems that transport people at velocities gradually approaching the speed of light. There are permanent communities on the moon, on Mars, and now even on some of the moons of the gas giant planets, Jupiter and Saturn. Robots have already visited the nearest star systems. Plans are being made for the first manned missions to these stars.

Unfortunately, this technological progress is tainted by the ego's identification with nationality. Instead of cooperating in these adventures, nations are still competing with each other to get to outer space first. Unfortunately, the militarization of the planets has also begun. Several nations have built military bases on the larger asteroids.

Much like the days of exploration of the earth by our ancestors when different nations competed with each other and even waged wars to populate, colonize, and steal the lands of other people, the nations of 2125 are engaged in a ruthless competition for the occupation of outer space. There has already been armed combat between robots and humans over various planets, moons, and asteroids in the solar system.

The SkyWoman encourages humanity to engage in another global dialogue in response to this second psychedrama.

Once again, emotion-waves of sadness wash across the earth. Most people have a sense that the SkyWoman is right, that human beings have at best only been able to tolerate each other for all of these centuries. Most people also now recognize, both emotionally and cognitively, the reality that global survival threats loom in their near future, including overpopulation, preparations for war, and accelerating climate change.

CHAPTER 25

Third Psychedrama: Love and Transformation

Key themes in scene:
1. Instead of acting out of the ego-based need to control and destroy other
people and other living things, or the fear-based position
of mere tolerance for the Other, people could also choose to act
out of love for themselves and the Other
2. The healing of the ego requires consciousness, or reverent awareness
3. If humanity heals ego and learns loving kindness,
transformation of humanity is possible

Location: Raj Ghat, New Delhi, India
Date: July 13, 2050

The third day of psychedrama meditation has arrived, and all over the world, people are preparing for this last event.

In Hainan, China, Bo Zhou sits with his new friends on the grass outside the hospital.

In Hobyo, Somalia, Duco Sagal does not have to call her children; they have been sitting all morning waiting for the next meditation.

In Salt Lake City, Sid, Matti, Benton, and Frederick are now joined by half of their neighborhood. People have prepared food, and folks are sitting in their backyard looking through the smoke and haze at the Wasatch Mountains across the valley.

In Loiyangalani on Lake Turkana, Kenya, the Great-Grandmothers are laughing together as they await the event. The wind has shifted, and a stiff breeze is carrying the smell of water from across the lake.

In New Delhi, the SkyWoman begins the meditation in the company of the Circle of 21.

"Welcome back, everyone. Let us begin our third and last psychedrama meditation. We are calling this meditation 'love and transformation.' We will now watch to see what happens if your species makes the leap to fulfill your spiritual potential.

"In this meditation, we will be viewing events both on the micro- and macrolevels. We will see future events in the lives of some individuals, as well as events shared collectively by all of your people. I will also be offering you some things I have learned from living a long life on my own home planet that apply to all intelligent beings."

After taking the world again through the beginning of the guided meditation, the SkyWoman brings everyone's attention to their own selves.

"Now I can take a look at myself. I see my energy field naturally interacting with the energy of other people, with the energy of the earth, and with the energy of the universe. This is my natural state of connectedness. It is my birthright, the connectedness every being has with the universe.

"Now I watch again to what happens when ego starts to eclipse a human being. The energetic connection goes away. In its place comes fear and the seeking for some kind of substitute for connection.

"I might ask, what am I afraid of? Perhaps I fear what other people think of me. Perhaps I fear the loss of what I have. Perhaps, ultimately, I fear death, which may seem like the ultimate disconnection, although it is not.

"And when I am not experiencing a connection with others and the rest of Creation, I can see how incredibly alone I can feel. And when I fight that aloneness, I experience loneliness, which is an attempt to escape from what is. Loneliness is frightening because it is a form of fear. And when I am in fear, I see how I seek out pleasures, security, blind obedience, or control as substitutes for connection. And I can see how these are poor substitutes; they only distract me momentarily from my sense of isolation from Creation. And I can see how, instead of experiencing natural connection again, I may instead seek the momentary relief of pleasure, security, blind obedience, or control for the rest of my life.

"My fellow travelers, it is not in itself bad or good to experience pleasure, seek security, follow an authority, or try to control things. These are natural human traits. However, identification is not connection, and identification with pleasure, security, obedience, or control just separates me from Creation and thus ultimately harms me, others, the global community, and the earth.

"Health is wholeness. When I live in connection with Creation, violence is impossible. As we will discuss during my visit with you on your planet. Living in connection is love. When I forget about my connection with Creation, my disconnection makes violence possible. Disconnection is violence because it is the separation of the whole.

"What is identification? It is the ego's way of dealing with connection by defining who I am through affiliation with something I am not. For example, I am not my house. I am not my country. I am not my religion. I am not even my body; although I may love these things, they are not me. Yet I can identify with any of these things to

the point where I become willing to give up my natural connection with Creation and with other people for an intense affiliation with a very small part of the whole. Then what I do not identify with becomes the enemy, whether it is someone in another house, in another country, with another religion, or with another body.

"It is possible to heal the ego to become whole again. It is possible for you to love yourselves, each other, and the ecosystems you live in. The work of healing is consciousness work, which is bringing reverent awareness to Creation in the only time and place that matters, the only time and place that, in fact, exists, which is right here, right now.

"Everything I just told you, you all already know. Let us watch now together what would happen if humans healed their egos right now."

Billions of people watch from space as Earth comes into view again. It is still the year 2050, but every person on Earth is now conscious of ego and healing ego.

In this meditation, the people of Earth have decided to invite the SkyWoman to support the cultivation of love and the process of transformation. There is a shift in consciousness on Earth that can be experienced energetically, even from up in space.

The people see the Circle of 21. The 21 participants look up at each other, each suddenly recognizing that they are all spiritual beings. Imam Hussein and Rabbi Galante both lean over to embrace each other. Nasteeho Sagal gets on her feet and begins a dance her mother taught her in Somalia.

They watch as a pilot flying a warplane over the Yellow Sea starts to cry as she realizes how close she came to killing others flying planes near her. The generals had forbidden them to listen to the SkyWoman, and yet this pilot had participated while in the air. There were other pilots who did the same.

They watch as a group of CEOs open their eyes and really look at each other for the first time across their big conference table. There is a long silence, and they stare in amazement as the dour president of GMU, Mr. Cheng shows some emotional vulnerability in front of the board.

Mr. Cheng composes himself and says, "Gentlemen; I have gained some insight into why I work so hard for wealth and power, and that I do not have to necessarily continue working this hard the rest of life."

They watch as Premier Petrov from Russia contacts Chairman Lau of China. When Premier Petrov sees the simulacrum of Chairman Lau, he stands up in his chair and says warmly, "Chairman Lau, I am so glad to see you and so glad we did not go to full-scale war!"

Watching the simulacrum of Premier Petrov, Chairman Lau smiles. "Ah, Premier. I am guessing that you were listening to the SkyWoman as I was this morning."

"Yes. And I imagine that you were as unhappy as I to see the aftermath of the world war we almost created. In that second psychedrama, our two great nations were reduced to wastelands."

"Yes. We both have children and grandchildren whom we love. It would be a shame to ruin their lives just because we elders have a quarrel or two with each other."

"Now, what if our two great nations helped lead the way to a new era of peace?"

Just then, the simulacrum of another person appears in the room. It is President Emily Browning from the United States.

"Good day, gentlemen. I don't see why the two of you men get to have all the fun of leading the world into a new era of peace by yourselves. I want in."

"Welcome, Madam President."

The scene shifts again. This time to the Vatican in Rome. Pope Luca is appearing in a hastily organized press conference. As millions of Catholics, joined by a billion other people, watch, the simulacrum of the pope appears in their homes, offices, and street corners.

"Hello to all of you. Most of us have just participated in the SkyWoman's three psychedrama meditations. I need to share with you what I have been thinking and feeling these past days. I realize now that the SkyWoman has not really told us anything that we did not already know. We have all known that love is the answer. Every faith system has taught this."

He smiles. "When I was a boy, my parents told me about a song that they saw performed by a popular band called the Beatles. The Beatles sang 'All You Need Is Love' to maybe a half billion viewers across the world. At the time, they performed to the largest live audience that had ever been seen before. John Lennon did not come up with this idea of love himself, of course. In fact, as I said, all the wisdom traditions of the world have taught about the importance of love for thousands of years. However, as the young people like to say here in Rome, we 'suck' at actually doing love.

"I just arrived back from this year's Religious World Summit in Japan, where clerics like me, from around the world met to talk about what is important. The SkyWoman has reminded me, and all of us, perhaps, that there is nothing more important than love. I would like to propose that all the religious leaders of the world meet together with our visitor from space so she can help us learn how to actually love each other."

As the people of Earth watch, the guided meditation shifts again. Everyone now sees a group of older women sitting in a circle on the ground. They are the Great-Grandmothers on the shore of Loiyangalani on Lake Turkana, Kenya. It is a colorful circle; each of the women wears the traditional dress of their native lands. They watch in silence as the SkyWoman descends toward them from across the great lake.

Now the SkyWoman is sitting with them, wrapped in her indigo energy field. She stands to speak.

"Great Grandmothers, you invited me to come and work with your people. Soon it will be time for me to leave. I will be asking you to lead the people of Earth in a series of dialogues. As I told you, we will call these talks the Eternity Dialogues.

"There are two reasons for the name. First, these conversations will address the choice that your people now have to make between eternal death and eternal life. And, second, to be effective, these conversations will need to go on indefinitely. Eternally. Dialogue is an ongoing process that never ends. It is eternal work.

"I will be asking the Great-Grandmothers to help me train the Circle of 21 and others to help facilitate these ongoing dialogues. The conversations will sometimes involve all people, and sometimes they will involve smaller groups.

"I ask you to do this work because you are the natural spiritual leaders of your race. Female humans are one of the few mammals on Earth who live a significant time after menopause, along with the elephants, the killer whales, and the pilot whales. The Great Mystery intended this so that the oldest women can lead the tribe with spiritual wisdom.

"You are not only the oldest women on Earth; you have also been doing your spiritual work for a very long time."

As the people of Earth watch, the meditation shifts again.

The SkyWoman speaks in everyone's mind again. *"My children, let us now see what life is like in one generation, 25 Earth years into the future, on a planet of life and transformation."*

From space, the people see an Earth that is a little cleaner. The desertization of the land masses has been reversed, and much of the North African and Asian continents that had become deserts are now green again. The oceans seem bluer. No plastics, sewage, or other waste have been allowed in the water for decades, and the wildlife is responding. The ice caps have stopped melting and the dead zones in the oceans that the great rivers created are starting to heal. Humans have found a way to cooperate with one another to use technology to heal the earth's ecosystems.

The scene shifts again, and the people see a group of Q'ero children playing in Ocongate, Peru. It is July and the dry season. At 4,572 meters altitude, the village is blessed with views of the Andes.

A bus appears on the road, kicking up dust that disappears quickly in the wind. The bus has a cargo of families. As they climb out, they are welcomed by the entire Q'ero community. Plenty of potatoes and munya tea are being prepared. The bus is full of privileged families of European descent who have traveled from Lima, the capital. They bring avocados, bread, and pastries with them.

As part of the ongoing Eternity Dialogues, they visit once a month as part of a series of dialogues designed to help transform historical trauma and foster reconciliation in Peru. The conversation topics range from the holocaust of the sixteenth-century European invasion to the decades of inequality and oppression in the nineteenth and twentieth centuries.

The people watch similar Eternity Dialogues in other locations on the planet. Conversations about historical trauma and reconciliation are being held in Lhasa in the Tibet Autonomous Region of China between Buddhist communities and their Chinese rulers. Parallel dialogues are being held between Navajo families and people of European descent in Shiprock, New Mexico; between the descendants of African slaves and the descendants of their masters in Charleston, South Carolina; and between people of Turkish and Armenian descent in Yerevan, Armenia.

The scene shifts to a neighborhood in Lahore in the Punjab region of Pakistan. There, a dialogue is in progress between families that identify as Muslim, Sikh, and Hindu.

Finally, everyone sees the old King David Hotel in Jerusalem. A hundred families are gathered from communities in Gaza, Tel Aviv, Cairo, Tehran, Egypt, and Jordan. All have lost loved ones to a century of seemingly endless terror attacks and reprisals. The dialogues focus on healing the shared grief and related historical trauma.

"Now, my fellow travelers, let us go ahead, as we have done before, and look 50 years into the future."

The people of Earth again first see their planet from space. Progress continues to be made in rewilding Earth. There are now what are being called "Global Reserves" in every nation and in every ocean. Many of the plant and animal species that were threatened with extinction are now beginning to recover in these reserves. From space, the planet seems to be increasingly green and blue, as regions of ecological ruin are being protected and nurtured.

The population of the earth is dropping as fair and transparent systems of family planning that empower individual choice have been developed in every nation. Negotiations are going on between nations for the elimination of national defense forces, including all weapons of mass destruction. Plans are being made for cooperative efforts to explore outer space.

The future Eternity Dialogues continue. Everyone on Earth is connected to the Mental Web, which now has reached a level of sophistication that allows people to connect to and then leave any of the millions of dialogues going on at any moment. Some participate in dialogues on the web, others participate more often in face-to-face dialogues.

"Now, my fellow travelers, let us go ahead, as we have done before, and look 75 years into the future."

The people see a huge spaceship circling a small unnamed planet in the triple star system Alpha Centauri. This planet, about the size of Earth, orbits Proxima Centauri, which is about four light-years from the sun.

The first human visitors to a planet in another star system are now landing. No longer is humanity divided by nationalities; the astronauts raise the flag of Earth with an image of the planet in front of a background of the galaxy. No longer is humanity divided by such differences as race, ethnicity, and gender; the starship crew represents every element of human diversity. No longer is humanity divided by political, religious, or other identities; crew members accept each other's backgrounds and beliefs, yet no individual member is lost in an ego identification with his or her backgrounds or beliefs.

And humanity is traveling into space without bringing the dark side of Ego with them. Instead of merely re-creating the problems on Earth, out into space, people are committed to staying in relationship with each other and Universe, through dialogue and service. Humanity has realized that any scientific or technological advance must be tempered by spiritual advance, characterized by consciousness, loving kindness, and commitment to the well being of all people, all life, and the ecosystems that support life.

Without the identification of ego, people on the ship are able to love who they want and to identify with any gender, race, culture, or other human difference that had formerly divided humanity.

The people return to Earth for another look into a distant possible future. The resources that had gone for millennium into preparations for war, into power and greed, and into other services of the ego have all been diverted to projects that benefit the well-being of all beings in the ecosystem of Earth. The population continues to drop, and every human now has meaningful work, adequate housing, and safe and healthy food, water, and air. More and more of the earth's land and seas are global resource parks where wild plants and animals live in healthy ecosystems. Many natural resources are now accessed from the incredibly rich asteroids that mostly orbit the sun between Mars and Jupiter.

Perhaps most significant, the people now see their descendants, grandchildren or even great-grandchildren. They are playing, perhaps in a garden. As children, they are already training in how to heal their egos. In fact, emotional and spiritual and social intelligence is valued as much as cognitive intelligence in the new school systems set up across the world. Children are educated in relational skills, including dialogue, and all high school students spend half of their time living in another country, doing service work with another culture.

Everyone is interconnected through the World Wide Mental Web. People still have privacy and individuality when they want it. They also can connect with other people anywhere on the planet when they wish.

There are no more nuclear weapons, no other weapons of mass destruction, and no standing military forces. A global police force, directed by a diverse global committee, enforces laws. The huge amount of resources previously used for military force is all devoted now to human and ecosystem well-being.

People can extend their lives indefinitely through immortality treatment, but everyone realizes that, without individual and collective development, such immortality is in itself shallow and ultimately dangerous. In fact, the highest educational priority is spiritual development—a spirituality based on connectedness and loving kindness.

"Now, my fellow travelers, you have seen three possible futures for your species of destruction, survival, and transformation. What future do you want? I want to hear

from all of you in the next twenty-four hours, one of your Earth days. If you decide on destruction, I will accept your decision and depart tomorrow for my home. If you decide on survival, you will also not need my help, because that has been the direction of your species for a long time, and you already know how to get along just enough for some of your species to survive. If you decide on transformation, we must start our work right away; we have little time left to wait."

CHAPTER 26

The Decision

Key themes in scene:
1. As humanity becomes conscious of its fears, shame,
and ego, it is likely to choose love and transformation
over destruction and mere survival
2. However, there will be people who have difficulty healing their
egos, and they may push back out of their fear and shame

Location: Raj Ghat, New Delhi, India
Date: July 14, 2050

Over the next 24 hours, the human species experienced a third global dialogue.

For those who have never participated in such a conversation before, it is hard to describe. Every person on Earth now has accessibility to each other and the SkyWoman through the Mental Network. Although individual conversations are possible, people continue to discover that there are also waves of dialogue available between small and incredibly large groups of people. People are able to participate in these "meta-dialogues," as they were soon named, and sense the overall emotional and spiritual experiences of thousands and even millions of people. Eventually, the Mental Network is renamed the "Psyche Network" since it is discovered that emotional and spiritual communications are at least as important and perhaps even more vital to human welfare than the mental.

Over the 24 hours since the SkyWoman led the world in the third psychedrama, the human species has been in a constant meta-dialogue. The response to the three alternative futures was overwhelming from the onset. The waves of emotion, thought, and spirit dance across the planet until a consensus starts to emerge.

Under the tent in Raj Ghat, the Circle of 21 listen to the global dialogue all night long until the direction of humanity becomes clear.

At the end of the 24-hour period, the SkyWoman returns to the Circle of 21.

"Hello, again my children. I would like to hear from you now. What do you want?"

Smiling, Aaradhya Sargretti says, "The people of Earth have chosen love and transformation. We ask you to help us move in that direction."

The SkyWoman responds, *"Thank you, Aaradhya. I am summoning the Great-Grandmothers from Africa to join the Circle of 21. We will spend a few days together here in India, and then we will begin the Eternity Dialogues."*

"Then we will all soon be returning to the Garden of Eden!" exclaims Rabbi Galante. "Halleluiah!"

Everyone in the room suddenly feels the SkyWoman's sadness as she responds, *"No, my brother, there will be more suffering that we will need to face in our days ahead."*

Not everyone on Earth was happy with the SkyWoman. She could sense the hostility, even in the Circle of 21.

The Eternity Dialogues

CHAPTER 27

The Ego Strikes Back

Key themes in scene:
1. The Ego (capitalized to include both the individual and collective)
is tenacious and requires constant consciousness to temper
2. It is possible to respond to attack without violence

Location: Raj Ghat, New Delhi, India
Date: July 15, 2050

Things seemed to finally be going a little better for humanity. As a convergence of such global survival threats as preparations for war, technological materialism, and climate change intensified, the SkyWoman, a refugee from a planet in deep crisis, suddenly arrived to offer help. After participating in the first global meditations and dialogues with the SkyWoman, the majority of the people of Earth had chosen love and transformation over death and survival. Plans were being made to begin a global conversation about how to transform historical trauma and build sustainable inner peace and collective well-being.

However, the collective human Ego does not like the SkyWoman's message. The Ego's tendency to identify with such beliefs as political affiliation, nationality, wealth and power, and religiosity seems to be hardwired in the human body-mind. Cunning and tenacious, the Ego is not willing to just go away because the Sky-Woman has arrived on the planet.

Now, using a variety of strategies, the Ego strikes back.

Location: New Delhi, India
Date: July 15, 2050

Hundreds, maybe millions of crickets are chirping in the gardens in waves of enthusiasm for just being alive.

It is dark now in New Delhi, but the heat and humidity of the day still linger. In the shadows, two small men in suits walk quietly up to the entrance of the SkyWoman's tent.

"Should we knock?" whispers Mr. Smythe.

"You can't knock on a tent, Smythe!" Mr. Brocktone whispers back.

At that moment, a now familiar voice returns, speaking inside their minds.

"Mr. Brocktone and Mr. Smythe. Please come in."

Startled, the two men cautiously pull the tent flap open and ease their heads inside. It is almost as dark inside as it is out in the gardens. A soft indigo light fills the space.

"You may take off your shoes at the entrance."

Compliantly, the men untie their dress shoes and leave them by the entrance. The SkyWoman appears to be sitting on the floor of the tent.

"You may sit with me if you like."

In their business suits, the men sit awkwardly. The last time they sat on the floor may have been when they were in their youth.

"Gentlemen, you do not have to bribe the guards outside to meet with me. You are welcome to ask to talk with me if you wish."

"We wouldn't do that ... I mean we wouldn't try to bribe someone ... uh ... your highness," whispers Mr. Smythe.

"Mr. Smythe, you would like to talk with me about something?"

"Uh, yes. We represent GMU, or Global Multinationals Unlimited, which is the largest corporate entity in the world. We have a business proposition for you. We would like to provide you with a private island for you to take permanent residence here on Earth. We would build a home to your specifications."

"Thank you, gentlemen, I am perfectly comfortable living in the tent that the people of India have generously offered me. Even if I wanted such a residence, I could not in good conscience take up so much space and resources when so many beings on your planet are homeless."

"Ah, yes," replies Mr. Brocktone. "Well, we are happy to provide you with *anything* you would like to make your stay here on Earth more ... uhm ... pleasant."

"Yes, ma'am," adds Mr. Smythe. "What *would* you like?"

The SkyWoman is quiet for what seems like an eternity to the two men, although it might have been only a few minutes.

"We are prepared to offer you anything you would like in return for you giving GMU exclusive property rights to all your advanced technologies," adds Mr. Smythe.

Although they cannot actually see the SkyWoman's face, they can feel her smile.

"Gentlemen, I come to your people to share my knowledge and skills and values in loving-kindness for all of you. I ask for nothing in return. I invited the two of you to New Delhi because you each have a potential gift for humanity. You see, everyone I

invited to the Circle of 21 has enormous spiritual ability. Most of you do not yet realize your own spiritual gifts, and I hope to help each of you develop them. Tonight, I want to guide the two of you in a psychedrama meditation that may help your development."

Looking at each other, feeling surprised and also honored, the two men hesitate. Then they both agree. After all, business is business. The SkyWoman helps them prepare for the meditation.

Then, as the two men sit on the floor, the guided imagery begins. Each man sees his own life, beginning with the experience of being a fetus in his mother's body.

Mr. Smythe sees his mother pregnant with him in 2005 in Ottawa, Canada. His father had abandoned her when he'd learned she was pregnant, and with no support system, she had to take care of her new baby on her own. He grew up in a public housing project.

Mr. Smythe's mother became depressed and at times suicidal. She started drinking more heavily and taking prescription drugs. He watches a scene when at the age of ten, he was so worried about his mother that he refused to go to school so he could stay at home and watch her.

After a series of suicide attempts and hospitalizations, she finally died of a drug overdose when Mr. Smythe was 17. The young Mr. Smythe blames his mother's death on his father's lack of responsibility and on poverty. He vows to never be poor. By the age of 24, he was already one of the wealthiest young men in Ottawa, investing in real estate and golf courses.

Never married, he kept his bisexuality a secret, because even in 2050, much of society still was uncomfortable with the many diverse human forms of love and sexuality.

For the first time in his life, Mr. Smythe goes deeply into his own addiction to power and wealth. He sees how power and wealth have been like his own heroin, giving him a short-lasting "fix," but never deeply satisfying. He starts to feel the tremendous sadness and fear that he had buried so long ago underneath his focus on his work.

Mr. Brocktone's psychedrama starts with his mother being pregnant in 2008. The oldest son of a wealthy family living along the "Gold Coast" of Lower Fairfield County, Connecticut, Mr. Brocktone was raised in a very conservative and religious environment. He was athletic and played quarterback for his high school team. He received a full athletic scholarship from Yale and entered the School of Management. While at Yale, he married a young woman from Smith College. His life appeared successful and even glamorous to himself and to others.

Then the SkyWoman shows Mr. Brocktone how as a boy he was always unable to talk with his parents about his feelings or thoughts. Nannies raised him for the most part since his father was usually in New York or abroad, supposedly on business, and his mother was very active in social events in the New England area. His parents stayed together, but a distant and often bitter marriage was hardly better for a young son than a difficult divorce might have been.

Mr. Brocktone's own marriage to his first wife ended in divorce in 2035 after she found out about his frequent affairs. With the SkyWoman's guidance, Mr. Brocktone also starts to feel the aloneness sadness and fear that has existed underneath his constant quest for fame and fortune.

As both men watch their psychedrama unfolding, they experience the suffering they'd had, but never experienced, in their lives. The SkyWoman watches their eyes get wet with tears.

"It is hard to feel again, after all these years. But remember, my friends, healing is wholing. To heal pain, we experience it. To become whole, we self-reflect and see ourselves and the world accurately, as you are both starting to do tonight.

"Now, finally, let me help you start to remember your spirituality. To do this, we will look at your deaths. Many of your people today only experience freedom from Ego at the time of their deaths, yet they fear the release of death as much as they hate the challenges of life. So they sit on the fence, if you will, between life and death, never journeying to explore either side of reality."

As the men start to get anxious, the SkyWoman smiles.

"It is OK. You will not actually die tonight. I know both of you have been receiving the immortality treatments, so in the meditation, you will see yourselves dying from accidental deaths."

Both men feel a powerful energetic hug of loving-kindness from the SkyWoman as the scenes in their minds change again. They both are in a plane that is landing in a heavy storm. As they watch, the plane crashes and bursts into flames.

Mr. Smythe sees himself, or what seems to be himself, looking down at his own body, which has died in the crash. As he rises higher in the air, he passes through the metal fuselage of the burning plane and up above the runway. He notices that for the first time in his existence, he is not worried about anything. In fact, there is a great peace within him, even though he has obviously just died tragically.

Mr. Brocktone watches as he struggles to get his seat belt off. Suddenly, he notices that he can pass right through his seat belt, leaving his body behind, which is lying broken on the seat. He too feels an unfamiliar sense of well-being and inner peace. The most surprising thing is that he does not feel angry anymore at anyone or anything.

"No wonder I am floating," he thinks to himself. "I must have been carrying tons of anger in my body, like heavy ballast in a ship at sea."

As the psychedrama closes, both men sit quietly on the floor. Both are teary eyed.

"I will sit with you here as long as you need me. Transformation is always possible in every moment, in every lifetime. You are both very talented men who are suffering from the same dis-ease, that we could call Egoitis, or the swelling of Ego. All intelligent beings can suffer from this. In your case, you both have substituted material wealth, fame, and power for spiritual wealth. Such a strategy can bring you short-term

pleasure but always also fails to bring long-term well-being, which is precisely why Egoitis is a root of all addictions.

"But you have an opportunity to make a difference. Like all who are privileged with material wealth, fame, and power, you especially have the response-ability to make a positive difference for people with less privilege. You will have an opportunity to do this, in your lifetimes and in the days ahead."

Location: Multiple locations around the world
Date: July 15, 2050

"How dare the SkyWoman come to Earth preaching this spiritual nonsense!"

"Yes, who does she think she is?"

"She has too much power!"

"I think we should do something!"

"Yes. But how do you fight an advanced civilization?"

A special closed meeting of the Steering Committee of the World Religious Summit is being held. Eleven religious clergy representing faith communities around the world are meeting together in simulacrum form.

"Well, isn't it a sin to worship a false idol?"

"Yes, and we could let our followers know that *they* are sinning as well if they follow her."

"Let us put out a joint declaration then. We can say that the SkyWoman represents a dangerous, evil, and blasphemous force sent here to Earth to test our faith."

"Yes, and anyone who follows her is excommunicated from the church!"

"Let's call in our marketing people and have them get started working on this. We can make the announcement at our new facility in Sri Lanka!"

Location: Brussels, Belgium
Date: July 15, 2050

A secret unofficial meeting of the European Union (EU) is also being held at about the same time. Highly ranked politicians from 11 EU nations are represented in simulacrum form.

"We believe that the SkyWoman is subverting national sovereignty and replacing it with some kind of world government, probably to be run by her and her planet."

"Such a move would not be in our interests. We would all become subordinate to this new global order."

"Indications are that perhaps she would favor India and other nations over Europe!"

"We must not let this happen."

"Yes. We must stop the Eternity Dialogues before they begin."

Location: Beijing, China
Date: July 15, 2050

Military leaders from the Eastern Pacific Rim Alliance (EPRA) are conferring with Chinese generals in Beijing. The leaders are all senior people in countries that have military arrangements with China through the EPRA.

"Are we on a secure line?"

"Yes, the politicians must never know what we are planning."

"Our armies have been compromised by this SkyWoman!"

"Yes, and our pilots are refusing to fly their planes or to fire on the enemy."

"We must stop the SkyWoman!"

"Our military believes that we can take out the SkyWoman with a nuclear attack, but we believe that such an attack is too risky and that India would retaliate. We are recommending a conventional surprise attack using our Special Space Forces Team. Their orders are to destroy the SkyWoman and the Circle of 21."

"Then we all approve?"

"Yes. Signal to begin the operation!"

Location: Secret Location on a Caribbean Island
Date: July 15, 2050

A small group of revolutionaries meets secretly in a boat offshore in a protected cove on an island in the Caribbean.

They represent the surviving remnants of the Global One organization.

"The SkyWoman has changed everything."

"Yes, but there are no guarantees that when she is in power she will follow any of our agendas for the world."

"We have come so far. Why back down now?"

"The safest thing to do is take her out."

"Yes. And we happen to have a robot and nuclear device, stored in the Pahargani, not far from her tent city."

Location: Istanbul, Turkey
Date: July 15, 2050

Mr. Cheng, president of GMU, is the wealthiest and most powerful man in the world. He is sitting in his office in Istanbul, Yurkey with some of his Central and South East Asian CEOs.

"Gentlemen, Mr. Brocktone and Mr. Smythe have apparently been turned by the SkyWoman and now seem to report to her. They were two of my best operatives.

Any of us could be next. I believe the SkyWoman represents the biggest danger to GMU that we have ever seen. What is your assessment?"

"Sir, our companies in India report that most of their workers are sympathetic to the SkyWoman. What's more, the government and military of India seem to be in her hands as well. My assessment is that you are correct, sir. She is a major threat."

The other men at the table nod solemnly.

"Very well, we are in agreement regarding the threat," Mr. Cheng says confidently. "I have a recommendation. We bought the rights to the Mental Web from Incheon National University in Korea. Let us completely shut down the network so that the SkyWoman cannot communicate with the people she has brainwashed. We can explain to the press that we are doing this for a scheduled maintenance and upgrade."

The board, as it always does, nods in silent agreement with Mr. Cheng.

Location: New Delhi, India
Date: July 15, 2050

The SkyWoman asks for a meeting with the Circle of 21 that evening.

She enters the room when everyone is there and then begins.

"Hello, my children. We are working together in a process of transformation. Whenever such a transformation begins, there will be people who feel more threatened than supportive of the process. Today, there are groups of people who are planning to disrupt our work of love and transformation. Some are planning violent attacks on this gathering. On the one hand, we want to have compassion for these people because they are operating out of Ego and do not know what they are really doing. On the other hand, it is also for us to protect our own transformation process because we have compassion for all of humanity. As leaders, we must never allow bullying. Bullying is a form of violence, which silences the other and therefore can only create monologue. The radical middle is possible. We can best protect ourselves and others from bullying and other violence not through more violence, but through loving-kindness, meditation, and dialogue.

"I propose we continue to do our work, reaching out to the world again and holding more meditations and dialogues. We will make a special effort to reach out first to those who currently wish us harm and invite them to meditate and dialogue with us."

Participants in the circle look at each other. Then Nasteeho Sagal leaps to her feet.

"I am with you SkyWoman!"

Billy Lee stands up next to her. "We are with you SkyWoman!"

The others agree.

"Thank you. Then let us set up the first invitation quickly. We do not have very much time. Their war machines are already airborne."

CHAPTER 28

Finding the Radical Middle

Key themes in scene:
1. There is always a radical middle between two positions, but the Ego can get in the way of finding it
2. When someone wishes to attack another, it can be seen as a request for help. The help needed is often the healing of past trauma.

Location: Raj Ghat, New Delhi, India
Date: July 16, 2050

The golden birthing of sunrise is reflected on the treetops as the members of the Circle of 21 siton the lawn in the garden at the invitation of the SkyWoman. She addresses the circle.

"Good morning. Deanna Bradley asked me why we always sit in a circle. There are several reasons. There are many circles in nature, such as the face of your moon, the iris of your eyes, and the view of the horizon as your turn around. Also, when we meet in a circle, everyone has a place and a voice. The circle is a container of a sacred space for meditation and dialogue, sacred in the sense that we all share a reverence and protection for the dialogue process.

"I called for us to meet this lovely morning because our project is being challenged. Please close your eyes, and I will show you some of the efforts now being organized against us."

The SkyWoman uses her powers to telepathically take the circle to a warship flying at an altitude of 100 km, far above the Bay of Bengal. Here Commander Wang of the Chinese Special Space Forces Team is preparing to initiate the tactical flight plan to New Delhi, India, that he was ordered to perform. His craft, the YellowBird, is the most advanced and most secret attack craft in the world, capable of incredible speed and stealth, and carrying nuclear-powered precision lasers. The

YellowBird is carrying the most advanced weaponry that Chinese and human technology has produced.

Then she shows them a small group of young men who are assembling a robot in a garage in Pahargani, a suburb of New Delhi. One of the men looks at the sleek missile designed to be fired by the robot.

"This rocket has enough nuclear material to put the SkyWoman and her crowd of admirers out of action permanently! Let's get this all in the truck and roll!"

The circle then sees an office building in Colombo, Sri Lanka, where a group of clergy members is preparing to make a major press release concerning their multi-faith perspective on the "sins of the SkyWoman." Some details have been leaked to the press, and there is a large gathering at the offices near the capitol grounds.

Next, they see a group of politicians in Brussels, Belgium. Here some leaders of the EU are also preparing to announce that they would like more time to deliberate on the SkyWoman's proposals before making a decision. Their hope is that by using stalling tactics enthusiasm for the SkyWoman will rapidly decline.

Finally, the SkyWoman shows how GMU is working behind the scenes to take complete control of the Mental Web as quickly as possible so that the SkyWoman cannot use it anymore for her meditations and dialogues. GMU puts pressure on Korea to agree to help speed up the takeover.

"Let us now have a dialogue. Today, please just speak out. Instead of using the talking stick, we will follow the dialogue guidelines we agreed on last night."

General Pomsky speaks. "This is outrageous! We must take out the enemy attack force and the terrorists immediately! I will alert the Russian military!"

Dr. Tasha Reeves, secretary of peace, responds. "It is outrageous, General Pomsky. But we know from history that violence has never brought us lasting deep peace. By 'deep' I mean that we not only end violence and war but also foster sustainable cooperation and loving-kindness."

Pastor Larah Jones nods in agreement. "Dr. Reeves is correct. We cannot let them destroy us, but we also must find an alternative to violence."

Mr. Kusumo from Indonesia turns to the SkyWoman. "Do you have the power to stop their bombs and robots from destroying us?"

The SkyWoman smiles again, and the group feels her smile since they still cannot see her face through the indigo light.

"Yes, I could use my physical power to stop them but that would not stop the next wave of identification. And then there will be another wave, and so on. If we use such physical force now, we would begin an ongoing war with the human Ego. By this I mean that if I only use physical power to stop these people, then the Ego's need to be in control, to protect itself and what it identifies with, would become even more powerful. Power, force, and violence cannot heal the Ego; they only feed it and make it stronger."

"Then what *do* we do, SkyWoman?" asks Nasteeho Sagal of Somalia.

The group looks at the SkyWoman. They feel her tears.

"Are you all right?" asks Yu Yan Zhou.

"Yes, thank you. I can smile, and laugh, and cry, just like all of you. Tears are not a sign of weakness, but a sign of strength. In my culture, beings of all social roles, gender identities, and cultural backgrounds are allowed to have and express the full range of emotions."

Billy Lee is also crying when he speaks. "Yes, in my culture, even the greatest warriors were allowed to cry in front of the tribe. But somehow, in the USA, even in 2050, crying is still seen as a weakness, especially for men. I cry now for my grandchildren, for my tribe, and for the human race. We have a historic opportunity to transform our lives and the lives of our descendants, and we are in danger of throwing and *blowing* it all away!"

"Thank you, Billy Lee. My fellow travelers, there is always a 'radical middle' response to every conflict. By this I mean that there is always a response that is neither aggressive or passive, that tells the truth, and that invites further dialogue rather than the monologue of violence. The radical middle can also be thought of as common ground between different viewpoints. In my language, we have a word that combines the meaning of your words 'empowerment' and 'assertiveness.' The radical middle uses what you could call 'empowered assertiveness' in our interactions with other human beings. The radical middle always involves a practice that your fourteenth Dalai Lama, Tenzin Gyatso, called 'loving-kindness,' so we hold the intent to support the highest good in our interactions with others.

"Walking in the radical middle is like walking along the top peak or ridge apex of a roof in a winter snowstorm. One sloped side is aggressive-aggression; on the other slope is avoidance or passive-aggression. It is, of course, very easy to slide down one side or another of such a slippery roof. To stay in the middle takes ongoing concentration.

"I propose that we use our combined spiritual power now to reach out to those who threaten us, in the spirit of the radical middle. The GMU has shut down the Mental Web, but we can use our combined power to contact and dialogue with any group on Earth. As we work together, I will help you all experience the work I am doing."

The SkyWoman has everyone in the group hold hands, as they sit in the warmth of the sun.

"We could say that, depending on the size of the people involved and how they stood, it would take between maybe twenty-seven and ninety million people to circle the earth while holding hands. There are enough people on Earth to circle the planet many times, in a spirit of loving-kindness and cooperation. This morning, we will start a process of uniting humanity by holding our hands together and using the power of loving-kindness toward ourselves, toward each other here in this beautiful garden, and toward every living thing on Earth."

Every member of the Circle of 21 starts to feel love from the SkyWoman.

"I do not make this love that you feel now from me. The love is flowing through me from the universe. Love is a gift from the Creator for all beings; it is part of the

energy of the universe that you all experienced when we did our first three psyche-drama meditations together.

"*Now let us focus first on the most immediate physical threat. A stealthy manned warship is now at the Kármán line, the edge of Earth's atmosphere. In a few minutes, it will be entering the Indian airspace. They are planning to laser these gardens and destroy us. The Indian Air Force will not be able to stop the craft and save us. Let us let loving-kindness flow through us toward the commander of that fleet, which now flies one hundred kilometers above Earth. I ask you all to focus your spiritual intent together as I reach out.*"

"What does that mean?" asks Phil.

"*To support me energetically is to focus your loving-kindness toward all of human-kind right now, and in particular Commander Wang. There is much spiritual power when people bring their loving intent together like this.*

As you do that, I will reach out to the commander."

"But how can you do that with the Mental Web now under the control of GMU?" asks Jean-Paul Martinez.

"*The power of your collective focus will support me. I will not always be here to help you take care of such emergencies as we have today. I will teach you how to work collectively to protect the peace you all want.*

"*So, as I dialogue with Commander Wang, I will at the same time invite you to experience the conversation. During this meditation, what I say you will hear, and what I see is what you will see.*

"*It is time. Please close your eyes and concentrate.*"

Commander Wang of the Chinese Special Space Forces Team is considered the "best of the best." He was chosen from hundreds of officers to command this special force because of his dedication, focus, and courage. He has always been successful in every mission he was asked to perform for his country. His superiors expect nothing less from him now. And, ironically, he will soon be challenged to act in a way that will be in the highest good, not only for China but also for all of humanity.

One of a kind, the YellowBird is the closest thing to a meld of human and AI ever produced. Commander Wang was one of the few human beings who had the skills and could stand the stress of sitting in a largely automated cockpit. He added the human element that made this AI warcraft superior to anything else on the planet.

Commander Wang does not know that the military is secretly planning his mission and that the government in Beijing is still unaware of their plot to kill the SkyWoman.

Commander Wang is getting ready to enter Indian airspace. All systems seem to be operating as planned. Then he starts to feel something. Not in his head, which is one of the best-trained and well-defended heads on the planet. Instead, he feels something in his *heart*. Something he never felt before in his life. He had grown up as an orphan. Not that all orphans feel unwanted, but he carried a deep sense of rejection and pain from his birth. His parents were young, just teenagers, and neither of them wanted him, but the mother was not allowed to have an abortion because of government policy at the time. Shamed by her family and community, the young mother left her own parents and birthed her son in another village. She left her baby at the doorstep of the local social services office and fled back home.

Commander Wang grew up in an orphanage in Shanghai and then was adopted out at the age of four. He was a difficult child, very angry and rebellious, and his frustrated parents sent him back to the orphanage. This pattern continued until he was 17, when he enlisted in the new Chinese Space Force.

He found a home in the military for the first time in his life. His ability to lead other men, his technological skills, and his raw courage were quickly recognized. He managed to control his anger just enough to be promoted. There was no man that Commander Wang feared.

But a powerful woman is now reaching out to him, and he is scared to death. It is perhaps because he has tried so hard to kill the feminine side inside himself that he fears the power of the feminine when it appears in his heart today.

As he sits in the cockpit of his command vehicle, he suddenly feels a loving presence inside. It is as if a man who has lived on the dark side of a moon all his life suddenly sees sunlight coming over the horizon. And somehow, he immediately knows who is reaching out to him. He heard in the briefing before the mission that the SkyWoman could visit people's minds. His officers said they could not be sure that she would not try to attack him with her spiritual powers.

But this does not feel like an attack. Instead, it feels like a gift, a crack in the wall, an opening in a cloudy sky. Something deep inside him wants to find out more about what may lie above the clouds.

"Hello?" he finds himself saying aloud.

"Hello, my friend. I am the one they call the SkyWoman, as you suspected."

"Why are you contacting me?" he replies, trembling now.

"I do not want to cause you harm, and I also do not want you to attack the gardens in New Delhi. I ask that you let me show you some stories from your own past and possible futures, as well as some of the stories about the people you are about to try to kill."

"But the mission?"

"You have fifteen more minutes before you begin your attack sequence. There is time to see much in fifteen minutes. Many times, when humans die, they are able to review their lives in seconds. After you see these stories, you will have a decision to make that will impact all of humanity."

He could hardly believe the words that were about to come out of his mouth. "OK, I agree. You can have fifteen minutes."

Wang turns off the communication sensors in the cockpit, temporarily disconnecting him from his superiors on the ground.

In the next minutes, drawing on the combined spiritual power of the Circle of 21, the SkyWoman shows Commander Wang some scenes from his own childhood, when he began to close his heart, and how his closed heart has only served to increase his suffering and the suffering of others.

Next, she shows him some of the stories of the people in the Circle of 21, stories of how they were all disappointed in life and how each of them responded to their suffering.

Then she shows him what would happen to the world if he successfully bombed Raj Ghat. It is not a pretty story. It is the story of World War III, the story of a bombed-out world. India would first retaliate against China. In a few minutes, all the nations in the world would become involved.

Finally, she shows him the truth about his mission. Wang sees his military superiors on the ground who have secretly planned this attack mission for their own immediate gain without the knowledge of the Chinese government.

Five minutes are left.

Commander Wang is powerfully conflicted. These stories have had an immediate effect on him. He is committed to his country and has sworn allegiance to the military, yet he now knows that the military has lied to him and betrayed his country.

The SkyWoman speaks again. *"Commander Wang, I know you are conflicted. I will show you one more thing, and then you must decide what you are going to do. I am going to show you what I can do with my spiritual power if I choose to."*

For a moment, Commander Wang is completely paralyzed. He has an uncontrollable urge to turn the fleet around and return to the secret airfield in the mountains. Before he gives the order to retreat, the SkyWoman lets him go.

"You see, I have the physical power to stop you, but I choose not to use it. There, now you are free."

"But why don't you just send me home or destroy me and escape your own death?" the commander asks.

"Sometimes, to have real peace and eternal life, one must be willing to die, my friend. I do not hate my life or wish to die, but I am willing to perish now if I must to show you that I mean you no harm. I challenge you now to do the right thing, to enlarge your identity from being an officer in the Chinese military, to being a member of the human race and a part of the future of your Mother Earth."

At about the same time, in a darkened underground room, a group of officers watch a screen in the Air Defense Command at Hindan Air Force Station, India.

Lieutenant Kumar points to a stealthy image on the screen traveling at incredible speed at an altitude of 100 km just outside of Indian airspace over the Bay of Bengal.

She stands up and exclaims, "This looks like an attack! Contact General Patel immediately." Then the lieutenant whispers, "No, I'm afraid it is too late. I think it is the Chinese; the machine has their signature. At least our new ionic radar could pick it up, but we were never briefed that they could come in so fast. Destination trajectory appears to be New Delhi. Estimated time of arrival in New Delhi is under one minute!"

They all stand in awe and terror as the image of the warship enters Indian airspace.

Then the blip suddenly starts to turn around and descend at incredibly high speed. The radar finally tracks it plunging into the Bay of Bengal, maybe 10 km off the coast of India.

The SkyWoman watches as Commander Wang makes his decision. She senses his plan.

"Commander Wang! You do not have to die. I will protect you if you want to land somewhere."

The commander replies, "No. I have made my decision. I cannot go back to China and surrender this technology to those who would destroy the world for their immediate gain. And I also cannot surrender our advanced technology to another nation. I wish for peace for everyone, including myself. At this moment, I have peace for the first time in my life. Thank you. Now I chose to die and see what is on the other side."

He watches the screen as the YellowBird heads toward the ocean. The AI keeps trying to stop the craft from self-destructing, but Wang overrides the controls.

"Blessings to you, Commander Wang!"

The Circle of 21 is silent. They sense the SkyWoman's sadness and understand that Wang made a choice of his own free will. Everyone else in the room is sad too over the loss of their friend.

CHAPTER 29

Life, Ego, and Death

Key themes in scene:
1. Death can be thought of as letting go of my
identification with the things that are not me
2. It is possible to face death by "dying each day" to what is
not me. Such work can also help free me to truly live

Location: Raj Ghat, New Delhi, India
Date: July 17, 2050

It is evening in New Delhi, and the SkyWoman has called the Circle of 21 again.

"My children, as I told you, I will not be working directly with you forever. I invite you to become students of spiritual power and eventually to start taking the lead yourselves, more and more, in the process of planetary transformation. I will be here to consult with you about finding the radical middle in resolving difficult conflict, but I want you to learn to work together to reach out to your fellow humans, especially to those who are in so much isolation and pain that they chose violence over love.

"You will not be alone, however. I have told you about the Great-Grandmothers. Just like they welcomed me to help your planet, I will be welcoming them now to come and work with all of you in helping the human race to heal itself. They will be your teachers and advisers in the years to come. It is time for the world to include women's voices in leadership, especially the voices of your aging women who have healed their Egos and have wisdom to share."

Billy Lee raises his hand.

"SkyWoman, as we talk about spirituality, I have a question. In many of the sacred traditions of the people of Earth, our ancestors taught that there is a 'Great Mystery' of spiritual energy in everything. This was called 'Maasauu' in Hopi and 'Wakantanka' in Lakota, for example."

"Yes, thank you, Billy Lee. The human race has largely forgotten about its own tribal origins and largely discounted the beliefs of those many now call 'primitive' people. The successes of your science and technology are remarkable. But your science and technology are also now associated with a materialism that denies the wisdom and wealth of Wakantanka and offers instead a reductionistic and monistic version of reality. Most humans thus live in spiritual poverty, in a world of separateness, superficial perception, and often-desperate pursuit of pleasure, power, and control.

"In my tradition, we also think of the universe as the Great Mystery. We know we cannot understand the entire universe and that humble acceptance allows us to ask the questions that can best inform our lives. For example, working with questions like, 'Why is there anything?' or 'Why am I here?' can help us make meaning and purpose in our lives."

Nasteeho Sagal of Somalia stands up, as she likes to do when she is excited, and she waves her hands as she speaks,

"My mother taught us that everything has a spirit consciousness. When I walk to the beach early in the morning to repair the nets, I feel that spirit consciousness in the waves, in the birds, in the wind."

"Yes, my beautiful daughter. I am so glad you are so sensitive to the world."

"My uncles always say I am oversensitive."

"Don't let anyone tell you that you are too sensitive. That is impossible. When people say that to you, they are saying something about themselves, usually that they are afraid of being seen by you, afraid of their own sensitivity, and afraid of what they feel inside. But sensitivity is a spiritual gift—a gift that requires feeling pain as well as joy. A sensate is not sensitive to only light; she also can see the shadows. No medicine is necessary to dull your senses, just consciousness, that is reverent awareness, of who you are. The Great-Grandmothers will help you protect your ability to feel and express feelings as you practice self-compassion.

"So today, we will be healing the Ego and practicing the work with some of the people who still want to destroy our transformational work."

President Emily Browning of the United States raises her hand.

"I just want to express my appreciation as we begin our work today. I want to thank you for coming to help the planet. I am also sorry that your own home planet was in such turmoil that you had to leave as a refugee."

"Thank you, President Browning. I believe that you and Prime Minister Saanvi Anand of India will use the political power you have to support the transformational process we are engaging in."

Prime Minister Saanvi Anand smiles and nods. "As do we, SkyWoman!"

"Our most pressing task is to work with the young men who are, as we speak, arranging to bring their weapons to these gardens. Let me show you."

The Circle of 21 now knows how to focus quickly when the SkyWoman is taking them into a meditation. She shows them the small group of young men who are driving their truck from Pahargani to New Delhi. Inside the truck is their war robot, ready to deliver its nuclear device.

Jean-Paul Martinez speaks. "Perhaps I can help. I know these men. They are part of my old organization, Global One. They are full of hate and tend to be impulsive. They have what my friend Dr. Tasha Reeves calls angry-young-man energy. I used to have the same energy."

Party Minister Yin from China raises his hand. "Yes, they remind me a little of Commander Wang, except they do not have his self-discipline. How do we help our young men get beyond their anger?"

Phil Parker of Salt Lake City raises his hand. "I still get angry. All the time. My anger seemed to help motivate me to expose the unethical practices of GMU. I'm not sure anger itself is a problem. It's about what you do with it, right?"

"Thank you, Phil. Yes, you are right. Anger is a strong emotion, which can move an intelligent being into motion. Think of the mother bear protecting her cubs. Or of the stories that emerged in the early part of this third millennium. For example, stories of your female superheroes such as 'Zena Warrior Princess,' 'Superwoman,' or 'Princess Mononoke' illustrate the positive power of anger when motivated for care and justice for others and used for good.

"Let us open up a conversation with the two young men in the truck, Aarav and Vihaan. Please feel free to enter into the conversation if you like."

Aarav and Vihaan are in their old red Toyota truck; the worst rust spots are painted over in a colorful turquoise. Vihaan is swearing at the traffic, which is at a standstill on the crowded highway to New Delhi. Both young men are nervous. Then they hear a voice in their heads.

"Hello, Aarav and Vihaan. Please do not be alarmed. This is the being you call the SkyWoman reaching out to both of you."

The men both look at each other.

"Did you hear that too?" asks Aarav.

Terrified, Vihaan can only nod.

"I am sitting here in the Raj Ghat gardens with the Circle of 21. We know you are coming to kill us. We ask that you have a dialogue and meditation with us. We do not want to distract your driving, especially on such a busy road, so it might be safer to pull off the road while we talk."

"What ... what do you want to talk about?" asks Aarav.

Aaradhya Sargretti enters the conversation. "Let's start with talking about your hearts."

Led by the SkyWoman, the Circle of 21 shows the two men who they really are. The young men see past their anger and look at the suffering they experienced when they watched their villages being destroyed by soldiers and later growing up in refugee camps. They feel the terrible pain of watching loved ones die.

The members of the Circle of 21 also reveal themselves. The young men meet each of the 21 participants and see into their hearts. In a few minutes, both Aarav and Vihaan are sobbing, as are many in the members of the Circle of 21.

"It is much harder to kill you now that we know you," explains Vihaan, shaking his head as he turns the truck around.

A few minutes later, he and Aarav surrender their weapons to the Indian authorities.

The SkyWoman then leads the Circle of 21 in doing similar work with the other people who wish to do them harm. The members watch as the SkyWoman works with the clergy in Colombo, Sri Lanka; the politicians in Brussels, Belgium; and the CEOs at GMU. She contacts each group in turn and holds up a psychological "mirror" in front of them, helping them to see themselves more accurately.

And as each "enemy" becomes more conscious, the members of the Circle of 21 watch in quiet awe as the people who wanted to harm them experience transformations.

Finally, Party Minister Yin breaks the silence. "Well, we have defeated the Ego then!"

"I'm not so sure, Prime Minister," responds Deanna Bradley. "The Ego is resilient."

Sitting next to her, Yu Yan Zhou slides her wrinkled hand across Deanna's back and hugs her. "This young woman is wise beyond her years. If I have learned anything in the long life I have been given, it is that my own Ego will live in me at least until I die. I can never kill it, and I no longer want to kill it, but I may be able to temper my Ego from time to time. In fact, ironically, just when I start to think that 'I got this. I have conquered my Ego,' I now realize that it is my Ego saying those words, once again needing to feel important, special, significant."

"Thank you, Yu Yan. Yes, the Ego appears to be a part of consciousness. Every being of my species on my home planet also has the gift and challenge of Ego."

"But how can Ego possibly be a gift, SkyWoman? We can all see now how Ego is the root of violence on our planet," asks Jean-Paul Martinez,

"Wonderful question, Jean-Paul. Everything that the Great Mystery gives each of us in our lives is both a gift and a challenge. We are here in the universe to further the collective development of Spirit. Ego is perhaps my biggest teacher because it constantly challenges me to go beyond my beliefs, to go beyond my illusion of a separate self, to go beyond all my self-importance and see the reality of everything. Without Ego, I would probably not seek the One, and I would certainly never find out what love, joy, and ecstasy are. Without the Ego of my enemy, I would not be challenged to learn to love myself and the Other."

"What are love, joy, and ecstasy then?" asks Phil Parker.

"I can tell you in words, Phil. But if you really want to find out, you can find out for yourself. Your question gives me an opportunity to talk with you more about

consciousness. Do not look for the answer only in your thoughts, however. As we have discussed, thoughts are always from the past, from past experience and conditioning, and cannot possibly in themselves tell us about the present reality.

"Our thoughts are not bad; they serve a purpose in our lives. Through thought, humans have created a vast technological society. But as we have said, the Ego easily identifies with beliefs, which, of course, are thoughts. And merely understanding something from an intellectual level may at times be a necessary first step, but it is not the same thing as understanding through consciousness, which requires intuitive knowing. Intuitive knowing uses not only the mind but also all ways of knowing available to the body-mind-spirit.

"For example, we all saw the clouds outside on our walk this morning. As you may know, those types of clouds are called 'cumulus clouds' by your scientists. As soon as I say to myself that I am seeing a cumulus cloud, I can easily lose the ability to actually see the real unique cloud above me in the present moment because my mind has already decided that it is experiencing something I learned about in the past.

"Perhaps look first for truth in the spaces between your thoughts, those moments when you are not thinking but are, in a sense, in 'empty space.' It is possible to see the world without thought. It might help to think about how much of our world is empty space. The scientists tell us that even the smallest atom, the hydrogen atom that makes up most of the stars that shine, is about 99.9999999999996 percent empty space. When you look up into the night sky, you can see how much of it is empty of stars. Find that empty space in you, the great space without human words."

"I wish I had your intuitive skills, SkyWoman, when I was working with my suicidal clients in San Francisco," Deanna says. "Maybe I could have saved them."

"Some people choose to end their lives rather than let go of the beliefs, choices, or relationships that are causing them suffering. We cannot judge them, and we cannot save them all.

"The fighter pilot today chose to die, and I honor his choice. He needed to let go of his conditioning around patriotism, masculinity, and duty. His consciousness had not yet developed to the point where he could imagine anything else left inside himself to replace that conditioning. In other words, like most humans, he was still very identified with his beliefs, his roles, and so on, and thus extremely uncomfortable with being in that 99.9999999999996 percent empty space that makes up everything and that makes up each of us.

"Every being is challenged every day, every moment, by the reality of life and death. We are naturally afraid of the apparent nothingness and emptiness of death, but we are just as frightened of the vulnerability and responsibility of living life. It is possible to be free from that fear when I am willing to die in each moment.

*"To die in each moment is to **let go of my identification with the things that are not me**, including my possessions, my roles, my body, and my thoughts and beliefs. Then I am able to see the universe the way it really is.*

"To live in the moment is the same thing.

"Today, my fellow travelers, we strive to help humanity live through this time of the Convergence by helping people die in the moment. We strive to die in the moment so we can truly live.

"Yes, in this sense, life and death are the same thing."

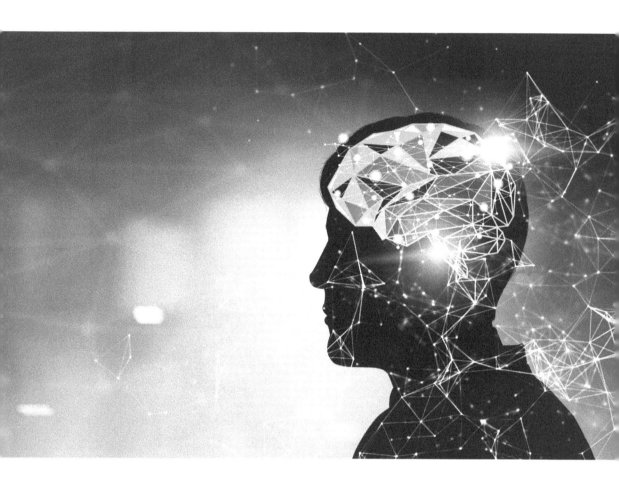

CHAPTER 30

Ego, Ecstasy, and Love

Key themes in scene:
1. Unconscious Ego identification can only give me
temporary pleasure and relief from pain
2. The work of making Ego consciousness can
help foster love, ecstasy, and joy

Location: Raj Ghat, New Delhi, India
Date: July 18, 2050

Nothing wrongs the world holds its collective breath, transformations are occurring everywhere.

The Indian Navy locates the wreckage of Commander Wang's YellowBird craft. When they inform the Chinse government, the Indian authorities learn that the Chinse leaders were as surprised as the Indian authorities were that the mission had been launched. Commander Wang is soon seen as a hero all over the world—a hero who averted a possible nuclear war between India and China by flying his ship into the Bay of Bengal.

The two young men, Aarav and Vihaan, who turned themselves in to the Indian military are arrested and held in a military installation in New Delhi. Prime Minister Saanvi Anand visits them. She embraces both men and thanks them for not exploding their device in the city. Suddenly, both men experience something neither of them has ever experienced before: the gratitude of a community. The prime minister invites them to join a national task force she is forming that will implement suggestions from the SkyWoman and the Circle of 21. Aarav and Vihaan accept her invitation.

In Colombo, Sri Lanka, a group of clergy members who were planning to incite their followers to rally against the SkyWoman now begin a second major press release. The world sees a small group of men with a completely different message—one of peace and reconciliation. With their new consciousness recently enhanced through their conversations with the SkyWoman and the Circle of 21, they are more willing to be vulnerable, and each speaks to the fear that was at the root of the group's anger toward the SkyWoman. They ask for forgiveness and promise to seek the highest good of all of humanity rather than to merely seek to preserve the power each had in his own faith community. They also admit that it will be difficult for all of them to resist the Ego and that they will be in lifelong "recovery" from their own "Egoitis."

A similar transformation occurs with the group of politicians in Brussels, Belgium. When people become conscious of the roots of their behavior, such Ego motivations as fear, envy, greed, and shame no longer have as much power as they did when they remained unnoticed, minimized, or denied. These politicians are at the beginning of that process of developing consciousness, and they are all starting to see the futile emptiness of the pursuit of power and control. None of them can forget the things the SkyWoman reminded them of:

"Power and control are actually your heroin, or your favorite drug, my fellow travelers. What I mean is that, when you are successful in gaining what seems like political power and control, it gives you a temporary 'high.' The Ego is in control again, and for a little while, you can forget about what your life is really like. While there is nothing wrong with wanting to change your experiences, it is helpful to be conscious of the price you pay for that temporary relief."

Mr. Schmidt from Germany and President Çelik from Turkey agree to send a public response to the SkyWoman and her Circle of 21, pledging the support of the European leaders for the work ahead.

Perhaps the biggest change of heart and mind occurs at GMU. It is not that businessmen in 2050 are necessarily eviler or more disturbed than other people on Earth. What puts them at risk of suffering from spiritual poverty, however, is their extreme material wealth.

The ten wealthiest CEOs at GMU have more resources available to them than about half of the other humans on Earth have between them. The temptation to accumulate and identify with such vast wealth, as the SkyWoman pointed out to them, has eclipsed their other motivations.

No one seemed to know anything about Mr. Cheng, the wealthiest and most powerful person on the planet. Most people assumed he was Chinese because of his surname. His associates knew he was very intelligent because he was fluent in at least four languages: Chinese, English, Russian, and Hindi. What stood out most about him was his ability to influence others. He had joined GMU as an associate CEO in 2046, and apparently in just a few years had become president of the organization.

The SkyWoman spent maybe an hour with Mr. Cheng, but in that time, she held a spiritual mirror in front of him and showed him his entire life. She started with the following words.

"Mr. Cheng, we meet again. Yes, I sensed your power on this planet when I first landed in India, and you sensed my power as well. I recognized that you have the unusual ability to quickly assess people's motivations, strengths, and weaknesses, and then to use your insights to manipulate their thoughts and behaviors. You have been frustrated because you cannot assess or control me, and you sense that I am the biggest threat to your hunger for total world domination. That assessment is only partially correct. Your biggest enemy is not me, or the associates and politicians who resent you, or the revolutionaries who want to kill you. Your biggest enemy is yourself.

"What do I mean? Let me take you on a trip inside the human you fear the most on this planet: yourself!

"The ancient shamans on Earth would sometimes offer tribal members a healing journey down into the earth. They would usually offer drumming as their fellow tribal member went into an ecstatic state and descended in meditation down into the earth, perhaps through a cave, a crack, or another opening. We will travel down also, down beneath your brilliant and busy cortex, through the limbic system, down below your neck and into your heart."

Mr. Cheng watched as his attention sunk below his immediate concerns about GMU, about the SkyWoman threat, about the politics of the Yellow Sea and everything else. He watched the energy of his brain and saw how little of his body, below his brain, that he was using. He sunk down through the limbic system and brain stem and then the spinal column toward his beating heart.

The energy of his heart seemed eclipsed. This, he realized, was Ego. He watched as the Ego eclipsed his entire being, telling him that power and wealth were the most important things. It was extremely painful to look past the Ego's protection and see inside his heart, which he had abandoned years ago as a refugee from China, swimming across the border in the dark with his parents, and watching his father get shot from behind and sinking in the water. He'd held on to his mother as they made it, finally, to the other shore, only to see that she had also taken a wound—a fatal wound. Then he was totally alone.

Alone. That was the story of his life. He lived always more alone than he wanted to be. He somehow made his way south to Thailand. Growing up on the bitter streets of Bangkok, by the age of ten, he had already learned how to manipulate others so that he could survive. He had no real friends because he trusted no one. He was determined to survive, and he did. There was nothing he was unwilling to do to survive.

His heart was broken, and it was closed. At night, when he found a place on the street to sleep, he would often look at the gleaming lights of the big office buildings in the Silom/Sathorn central business district of the city. He would fall sleep angry that the computers, desks, and chairs slept in far better conditions than he did every night. In fact, when he became wealthy, the first building he bought was in Silom/Sathorn. But he did not offer the building space for the homeless. Instead, he worked very hard, buying up properties and building an immense fortune in real estate around the world. Instead of becoming a wounded healer, he became a wounded destroyer.

Transformation can happen in any life, at any time. But the heart and mind of Mr. Cheng were not only closed but also guarded by a thick fortress of anger, all covered up by his impenetrable gaze. For him, if just one tear of sadness leaked out of his hardened eyes, it felt as if the Three Gorges Dam on the Yangtze was about ready to burst and flood half of China.

The SkyWoman understood this, and she held a space for Mr. Cheng to do his work, offering him her loving kindness. He cried later for hours in the privacy of his office.

The members of the Circle of 21 watch the beginnings of Mr. Cheng's transformation.

Mr. Brocktone is deeply affected as he watches his mentor, Mr. Cheng, weeping uncontrollably in his office, on the 68th floor of the Cheng Tower, formally the Thailand Trump Tower, in downtown Bangkok.

"My God. Is he ... is he going to be all right?"

Mr. Smythe is shaking next to his friend Brocktone. "Brocktone, I actually think ... for the first time—now that I know what he has gone through and seeing his story—I feel some compassion for that old man."

"And perhaps some compassion for yourself as well, Smythe?" responds Brocktone.

"Yes, Mr. Smythe" adds Dr. Adele Dubois. "I hated Mr. Cheng after he sent you and Mr. Brocktone to Korea to take control of our project. I hated both of you as well. I did not realize the price I was paying for my hatred until right now. I was so Ego-identified with making the Mental Web available to the world that I forgot that transformation only comes from love. Hatred is a poison that is so easily taken."

Dr. Jiu Kang nods in agreement. "Thank you, Dr. Dubois for being so honest. I have also been struggling with similar feelings."

The SkyWoman joins in the conversation.

"Thank you all for being willing to look at yourselves! Remember that consciousness is reverent awareness. I want to not only see myself and the world but also to see everything through friendly eyes, through the heart-lens of loving-kindness. For what good does it do to see myself or the world accurately if I hate what I see?

"And when I see myself through the lens of loving-kindness, it is possible to experience what some of your ancestors called 'ecstasy.' Ecstasy came from the root expression 'to stand beside myself' in the ancient Greek. In other words, ecstasy is what humans can experience when they see the world through the eyes of love instead of through the eyes of unhealed Ego. When Ego runs my life, I cannot 'stand beside myself' can I? Ecstasy may be the greatest joy that humans or any conscious beings can experience—a joy not dependent on belief or circumstances or so-called good luck or bad luck."

"I would like this ecstasy," Mr. Kusumo interjects. "Please tell us how to get it."

"Mr. Kusumo, remember when you were a young man in the military service and your platoon was ambushed in the jungle by insurgents?"

"Yes, but how did you know?"

"Do you remember, Mr. Kusumo, how you felt and what you said to yourself?"

The group is silent as Mr. Kusumo starts to open up. No one has ever seen him vulnerable, talking openly about his emotions or thoughts.

"I was eighteen and already a sergeant in my platoon. Yes, we were on the trail of insurgents walking through a heavy jungle in Sumatra. My lead soldier, who was maybe three meters ahead of me, was suddenly engulfed in flames as he stepped on a land mine. The whole forest became a living hell as we took mortar and small-arms fire from what seemed like all directions. Half of my men were wounded or killed in the first seconds of that ambush. We took cover as best we could. We called for help, but only five of my men were still alive by the time the hovercraft arrived to rescue us. Images of that time still haunt me every day."

"What were you thinking and feeling at that moment, Mr. Kusumo?"

"All I could think of was I would do *anything* to get out of there alive."

"Yes, and you will need to want the joy of ecstasy just as much as you wanted life back then, and you will need to focus on ecstasy just as much as you focused on life back then if you are to find it. Otherwise, it will be easy to continue to seek short-term pleasures and distractions. Most of the humans on your planet seem to be addicted to some kind of coping mechanism that serves to help them avoid the difficult thoughts and feelings they have inside. These coping mechanisms might include such obvious pleasures as drugs, sex, fast food, or digital entertainment, but they also could be related to focusing on their vocations, their families, or their homes. The work of ecstasy is the work we have been talking about since I came to visit you all; we strive to see the world the way it is and to be OK with what happens.

"When I am conscious of Ego, I become free to truly love myself and others. This is because I become able to see how I actually do not love yet. For example, when I see that duty is an Ego identification that arises out of fear, then I see that duty to my family, duty to my country, or any duty is not love. Similarly, dependence on another person, or possessiveness, or domination of another person is not love either.

"Love, ecstasy, and joy are thus all related, my children, and all available to us as we do our work of consciousness. My fellow travelers, it is not easy having a consciousness that is aware of itself, but it is also a great blessing. Can you feel that yet?"

"Yes, I can!" volunteers Nasteeho Sagal. "But, SkyWoman, can you please tell us more about yourself and your own home planet?"

"And how and why you came to Earth?" adds Jean-Paul Martinez.

"And how the Great-Grandmothers contacted you?" asks Yu Yan Zhou.

"Yes. I shared with you all that I am a refugee from my own planet, which was consumed by Ego and headed toward destruction. My only wish is to help your human race to transform through loving kindness. I plan to show you more about myself soon. Perhaps more than you may want to know."

CHAPTER 31

Global Dialogues

Key themes in scene:
1. It is possible for human beings to live in connection
with each other and with the rest of Creation
2. The dialogue ground rules can help guide the dialogue process

Location: Raj Ghat, New Delhi, India
Date: July 19, 2050

Most of the members of the Circle of 21 are blown away by all that has happened since they first heard a summons to New Delhi from the SkyWoman. In only a few days, the world seems so different. Is it more because of what has changed on the planet or more because of what has changed inside of them? They are unsure.

The people of Earth are invited to connect through the World Wide Mental Web to hear the SkyWoman begin the Eternity Dialogues at the next meeting of the Circle of 21. Still wrapped in her indigo light, she begins the conversation by welcoming everyone.

"Hello, people of Earth. Welcome to our circle again. Also welcome to the Great-Grandmothers, a group of women I have told you about who are the ones who first invited me to Earth. You can see them sitting in the center of the Circle of 21. They like to sit on the floor. These two circles of people will be assisting me in working with the people of Earth in this new era of transformation.

"The members of the Circle of 21 will always be transparent in all of their activities. The world needs leaders who are willing to show vulnerability as well as strength. So we will now show you how we contacted and worked with the people who wished to do us harm."

The people watch as they are shown the activities of the SkyWoman and the Circle of 21 in dealing with the military, economic, political, and psychological threats of the past few days.

They see, for example, the interactions between Mr. Smythe and Mr. Brocktone in her tent. They watch the SkyWoman reach out to Commander Wang as he flies over the Bay of Bengal and see his fiery death. They see Aarav and Vihaan turn their truck around on the highway in India. Other scenes in Europe, Asia, and across the world are observed. Then the SkyWoman speaks again.

"As you can see, my children, it is possible to meet hate with consciousness and loving-kindness. We acknowledge that there is always a short-term risk in the practice of nonviolence. However, the practice of meeting violence with more violence always carries greater long-term risk of endless repetition of and further escalation of mutual destruction.

"In the past days, you, the people of Earth, were presented with three alternative futures of destruction, survival, and transformation. You chose transformation. Now it is time to begin the work of transformation—an eternal project that has no end. We want to invite you to begin what we are calling the Eternity Dialogues.

"The purpose of dialogue is to create relationships—the kinds of relationships that are necessary for transformation. These include relationships between individuals, between institutions and communities, and between humans and the rest of the universe.

"The kinds of challenges and discoveries that lie ahead for your species require what we could call transformative relationships. It took cooperation when you made tools for hunting, built your pyramids, and created machines to fight your wars. However, the primary motivation for such cooperation was usually fear. There was fear of hunger and starvation, fear of death, fear of other tribes, fear of vulnerability, and fear of fear itself.

"Transformative relationships invite cooperation based on loving-kindness. Dialogue practice can help foster such cooperation. It will take such a deeper cooperation to enter the coming era of transformation.

"Is it possible for the motivation of cooperation to move from fear to love?

"As we said before, we use the word 'eternity' in part because your species has developed the technologies of eternal life and of death. Without dialogue, without relationship, eternal life becomes an avoidance of both life and death. There are no shortcuts to what you call eternal life; there is no material technology that can create eternal life because you already have it.

"In addition, the Eternity Dialogues will be an eternal project for your species. This is because the work is a spiritual practice, and any spiritual practice involves ongoing commitment. The work is not easy, and the speed and form that transformation takes may be frustrating, but the outcome can be incredible. As you have seen, the price of not doing the work is ultimately the destruction of your species.

"The two most important elements in dialogue are speaking respectfully and listening for understanding. To listen for understanding and speak respectfully, we watch how Ego is constantly getting in the way of our ability to see ourselves and each other

accurately. We realize that Ego separates us from each other and from the universe. As we heal Ego through consciousness, we become free to affirm our coexistence as interconnected parts of this beautiful universe. There are other ground rules that we will share with all of you; most are simple and can be taught to children in school and in their homes.

"I have studied your home languages, and they can tell you where your expressions come from and help you understand them. For example, it may help to think of 'listening for understanding' as meaning 'to be close to another' by seeing things 'from where the other person stands,' which is related to your ancient Greek word 'epistamai.'

And respect, from your ancient Latin word 'respectere,' means 'to see again,' which helps us think of respect as an ongoing, eternal process of seeing myself and others accurately and perceptively in the present moment, with 'new eyes.'

"Let us see now through meditation what an energetic view of global dialogue looks like. By energetic view, we mean that we are seeing how the energy of the universe behaves when humans make the transformation from an Ego-centered race to a love-centered race of beings."

The SkyWoman again guides the Circle of 21 and the people of Earth in meditation. This visualization begins with a view of Earth from the vantage point of the moon's orbit. The SkyWoman first shows the energy patterns on Earth at about 4.5 billion years ago, when the time of intense bombardment of all of the inner planets by other objects was finally quieting down. The young Earth still looks barren of life. The planet glows with a soft halo of energy as it orbits the young sun.

Then, as the planet cools, the first obvious life appears, seeded from space. The simple life-forms appear connected with each other and the planet, like a glowing, rotating sphere of webbed light filaments. As life-forms multiply and evolve, the filaments of light that connect them together become more abundant. By the time of the dinosaurs, about 150 million years ago, there are so many life-forms on the surface of the earth that the whole sphere is lit up in shimmering light like a slowly rotating ornament.

When the first hominids appear over six million years ago, something happens to the light display. The hominids still, of course, are connected to the universe like all other creatures, but as the the precursors of human Ego start to emerge, the awareness of the connection diminishes. At about 200,000 years ago, the Ego as humans know it today, is born.

Ironically, the species that eventually conquers the planet is the same species that first loses the sense of connection with the planet. The Ego, which initially gave humans an advantage in survival eventually became the mechanism that separated humans from each other and the universe.

As human life began to cover the earth, the intense spherical display of light starts to develop areas of darkness as connections are eclipsed by Ego. Like a brain in dementia where neurons become isolated from each other and the body systems, human life became isolated from the web of life. As humans start to build villages and then cites, the areas of darkness increase as the connections of light go out.

Many people participating in the meditation are struck by how the display looks like the opposite of what the earth looks like at night from above. From the perspective of the human eye, when looking down at the surface of Earth from space at night, the concentrations of artificial light from such great cities as Tokyo, Mexico City, and replace London illuminate those urban areas; the more rural areas and the great oceans are dark. But from the energetic perspective that the SkyWoman is revealing to humanity, the view of the interconnecting energy of the world is just the opposite; where humans live, the light energy is dimmed.

The SkyWoman pauses. She looks around the Circle of 21 and poses a question.

"Is it inevitable that human progress decreases our birthright of spiritual connection with the universe?"

"No," answers Aadhya Amin, the lead curator of the gardens at Raj Ghat. "If we can design gardens that honor creation, like here at Raj Ghat, we can also design cites that honor creation."

"She is right!" shouts Nasteeho Sagal from Somalia. "We can find ways to live in harmony with Mother Earth! And with each other!"

The members of the Circle of 21 can feel the SkyWoman's smile as she responds.

"Thank you, my fellow travelers. Yes, it is possible for human beings to live in connection with each other and with the rest of Creation if you decide to heal Ego.

"Now, please watch what I mean. Watch as I show you an energetic view of your home planet, Earth, as humans heal Ego and create transformative relationships."

The people of Earth watch as the earth changes again. Instead of seeing patches of darkness where the great urban areas lie, the concentrations of human beings are illuminated in complex webs of light that interconnect across the surface of the planet. These interconenctions show how humans are learning how to live with and support the complex ecological systems that support all life. The view is stunning to the billions of people who are participating in the meditation.

"Now, let us begin the Eternity Dialogues. The first dialogue will begin with meditation. Dialogue is always both internal and external. Self-reflection is a dialogue with myself, and it prepares me for dialogue with others. As I know myself better, I am better able to heal my Ego, see things the way they are, and speak my truth to others. As we have discussed, dialogue and meditation are thus interconnected.

"The focus of the meditation is identifications. Each of us around the world are invited to reflect on what your own strongest identifications are now. We will systematically review a number of possible areas to research. Remember that identification is when the Ego believes 'that thing is me, and I am that thing.'

"We will start with material possessions. There is nothing wrong with having such things as food, housing, cars, toys, and so on. I can, however, see how much I identify with those things, and I can ask myself, if I had to, could I let go of my possessions

today? Perhaps my home catches on fire, or there is an earthquake, or maybe I die today. How difficult would it be to let go of my possessions?

"Next, we will look at social roles. Maybe I am a grandmother, father, or a wife, or a grounds keeper, and so on. I can ask the same question: Could I let go of my roles today if I had to?"

The SkyWoman walks the people of Earth and the members of the Circle of 21 through a number of other possible identifications. Together, they look at wealth, health, power, status, beauty, culture, race, nationality, and vocation. Then they look at belief.

"Finally, my children, let us look at belief. Consider the things you believe in, particularly your most cherished beliefs. These may be about your faith system, your political affiliation, your personal story that you tell yourself about your own life, or your own personal hierarchy of values. Can you let those go too?

"We saved beliefs until the end because most of us have our greatest attachments to beliefs. When we begin the Eternity Dialogues, most of you will be triggered emotionally by comments from others that challenge the beliefs that you identify with."

Although the work is difficult, most of the people of Earth are able to succeed, in part, because they know that they are not alone in doing that work.

"And now, through a combination of my telepathic power and the work of our technicians, we will be connecting each of you up with a random group of seven other people on the planet whom you have never met. The seven other people will represent different identifications, including genders, sexual orientations, ages, cultures, and races, than you have. Each of you will introduce yourself to the group, and then you will take turns sharing what you experienced and learned in the self-reflection exercise we just did. If any group needs some help with facilitation, one of us in the Circle of 21 or the Circle of Great Grandmothers will come to your assistance."

And thus the Eternity Dialogues begin. For the first time on the planet, most of humanity is participating in dialogues for the purpose of planetary transformation. The participants can not only "hear" each other's voices mentally (immediately translated, if necessary, into their own languages) but also "see" each other's images and immediate surroundings in their minds.

In one of the more than one billion dialogues going on simultaneously, in a typical meeting of eight human beings, the conversation is going like this:

A young woman Africa begins.

"Hello to all of you. My name is Mado. I am twenty-two years old and live in the Gamboma, Congo, with my husband and babies. The greatest identification I have is with my children, Divin, who is one-year-old, and Redina, who is two. I cannot imagine ever giving my children up, although often I can imagine kicking their father out of the house when he is acting like a child!"

There is good-natured laughter in the group and then an older gentleman speaks next.

"Hello to all of you. I never imagined that I would live to see this wonderful day when we are all meeting like this out of love! My parents named me Batbayar, which means 'strong joy' in our native language in Mongolia. I was their first child, and they were very happy when I was born. They were about your age, Mado, when I was born. They are both now passed. My mother recently died, and we gave her what we call a 'sky burial' during which my mother's spirit moved on. Maybe I am most attached to her. I identify as her son, and I miss her terribly."

Then a woman's voice joins the conversation.

"Hello to all of you. My name is Ratu, and I was born in Jakarta, Indonesia, on September 12, 2001. It was the day after the 9/11 attacks in New York City, and my parents told me that they were afraid at the time that there would be another terrible world war. I became a businesswoman, and I have to say, I have become quite successful.

"I live in Shanghai, China, most of the time, where I manage some of my biggest businesses. I suppose I am a bit embarrassed to say that I do not identify with people as much as I do with money, status, and power. I hope no one here makes a judgment about me. I want to believe that we all will be respectful of each other, as the SkyWoman asked us to be."

Just then, they are joined by another, much older woman.

"Hello to all of you. I am Aaradhya Sargretti, one of the members of the Circle of 21 and a member of the Great-Grandmothers that the SkyWoman talked about today. I want to join you just for a moment because I felt the discomfort in your meeting and have something to share.

"I have my identifications, yes, like all of you. I am a human being, like all of you, just a little bit older. I want to say to all of you, and especially to Ratu, that there is no reason to feel guilt and shame about what you identify with. Guilt in much of world is actually fear of punishment, and there should be no punishment for anything people experience inside themselves since we do not have control over that in the present moment. We only have a choice over how we chose to view the present situation and how we chose to act in that situation. Some of my Buddhist friends say that guilt is 'the refusal to see things the way they are,' and I like that definition because guilt is always a thought-based experience up in our heads, which can take us away from how we are actually feeling in the moment. As the human race transforms itself, we will not need guilt anymore to control ourselves and others. Guilt is a fear-based mechanism that was used for thousands of years to control the tribe. Guilt is not love and is, therefore, ultimately not helpful. When we act out of fear, the outcomes of our behaviors tend to be negative. We will be learning how to base our attitudes and actions on loving-kindness instead.

"Regarding shame, which is the feeling of inferiority that almost all humans have, this is just a basic Ego function. Whenever we compare ourselves to others, whether it is to feel inferior or superior, it is Ego doing its work. Such comparisons are ultimately unhelpful and destructive. Beginning with our early evolution, humans used shame to keep tribal members and then communities, as well as nations, in line. The problem is that any comparison between the relative value of two people or of two peoples is neither helpful nor true. Self-hatred and hatred of others are the same thing. Unhealed shame, which is shame yet unseen, results in both self-hatred and hatred of others. Healthy shame is simply seeing and accepting our strengths and limitations. The human race will be able to move beyond shame-based social control to simply seeing the world the way it is and living in loving-kindness toward ourselves and others."

"Thank you, Great-Grandmother," says Mado, "for spending time with our group."

"You are welcome. Know that I love all of you. And please also know that I am visiting many thousands of groups today, many at the same time, so I need to go."

And then she is gone.

CHAPTER 32

Local Dialogues

Key themes in scene:
1. Transformation to inclusivity can occur in
any family, organization, or community
2. Dialogue can help foster such transformations
3. Dialogue can have many forms, including both local and global settings

Sometimes, it may be easier to act one's way into new ways of thinking than to try to think one's way into new ways of acting. There were now many opportunities for the people of Earth to practice new ways of interacting with other people who were different from them.

In the following weeks, the SkyWoman facilitates more "global dialogues" in which humans interacted with others they have never met, often with different faith systems, political affiliations, ethnic backgrounds, and cultural practices. Many of these dialogues are done through the Mental Web.

She also creates opportunities for "local dialogues" between people who already know each other. Many members of the Circle of 21 return to their homes and work environments, and participate in such local dialogues with their colleagues, families, or friends. Many of these dialogues are done face to face.

New Delhi, India
Date: July 24, 2050

The Indian sun warms the gardens as the morning birds start to sing. The Great-Grandmothers sit in a circle outside the SkyWoman's tent. Aaradhya Sargretti begins the dialogue.

"Welcome my sisters! Let me summarize what has happened since we last met in a circle in Africa. The SkyWoman accepted our invitation and has led the people of Earth in meditation and dialogue. The people of Earth have chosen to cocreate a planet of transformative relationships.

"Our work is not finished, however. Instead, it has now just beginning. We will be leading the human race in dialogue for generations to come."

The other women all nod in silent agreement.

"Finally, you all remember that, before the SkyWoman came, we had experienced similar dreams. In my dream, I was walking in the morning when I saw a great stairway in the sky overhead descending to a spot at my feet. As a huge crowd of people assembled around me, praying and chanting, I saw a figure walking down slowly toward me who turned out to be me. I have been meditating on this dream and now see it as a message that the work we need to do here on Earth must start with me. I cannot look to the SkyWoman or to anyone else to deliver me.

"Thank you for listening to me. I have brought my talking stick. Now I want to hear from any of you who may wish to speak."

One of the great-grandmothers takes the stick. "Welcome back to our circle, Aaradhya. I am proud of the work you have done to help bring about the changes that have happened since you left. I hear what you have said about the dream we have all had. I have a similar sense about the dream and only want to add that I think this dream can empower all of us on the earth to each take responsibility for the work we all need to do to transform our species."

There are nods of agreement around the circle.

Downtown San Francisco, California
Date: July 24, 2050

When she was fired, Deanna Bradley never imagined that she would ever be sitting again at the table in the meeting room at Greater Bay Area Biotech, much less at the head of the table. But Randy Snyder, the clinic manager, had picked her up at the airport and driven her directly to the Greater Bay Area Biotech office downtown.

As Deanna walks in the meeting room, Dr. Yin, the clinic medical director, gives her a hug.

"Please have a seat, Deanna," he says as he walks her to the empty chair.

Dr. Delores Walker, the staff psychiatrist leads a round of applause as Deanna sits down.

"Welcome back, Ms. Bradley," she says a little stiffly as she tries to smile.

Dr. Walker was never very good at expressing warmth to her colleagues or patients, Deanna thinks to herself as she accepts the chair. She looks around the room slowly, nodding to each of the people she once called her colleagues.

"I want to thank you for inviting me back to the office," she starts. "I have accepted your invitation because it is important that we talk about our work with the immortality treatments. I understand that this meeting is being beamed to our other clinic locations. I want to invite everyone to participate in this conversation. We are putting the SkyWoman's dialogue guidelines up on the simulacrum to help everyone remember what they are.

"I want to start by saying that I have had time to meditate on the suicide of Mr. Hauser, who you will remember was our first patient at the clinic. Before he killed himself, he told me, 'I was so afraid of death. And now that the threat of death is gone, I have realized I am even more scared of life.' The SkyWoman has taught me that most people are indeed afraid of life and death. I am now more and more convinced that we must incorporate a program of meditation and dialogue for all of our patients both before they begin the immortality treatments and during the treatments themselves. We can teach people how to die to the things they identify with, such as their homes, their cars, their roles, and their beliefs, so that they can face death and truly live. This will be a required prerequisite for the immortality treatments. Now I want to hear from all of you."

Randy Snyder looks around the room as he speaks. "I want to apologize to you in front of everyone for firing you, Deanna. I hope you will consider coming back to lead us in our work with our clients. I am not sure I understand yet what this spiritual work is that the patients need, but I want to learn."

Location: Buenos Aires, Argentina, Puerto Madero district
Date: July 24, 2050

Mr. Cheng is waiting with the rest of the board of directors in the executive suite of GMU as Mr. Smythe and Mr. Brocktone arrive.

"Welcome back, gentlemen," he says.

Both Smythe and Brocktone immediately sense something different in the office. It isn't the participants. The same faces are there, as always. The room itself is still the same. Is it Mr. Cheng who is different, or perhaps they all have changed?

Mr. Smythe breaks the silence. "We have come back to facilitate a dialogue with the board regarding how we can now be of service to the people of Earth. We are the most powerful men on the planet, and we have a responsibility to help mankind."

Everyone looks at Mr. Cheng. As president of GMU, he had always dominated every conversation in the board room.

Everyone notices the shocking fact that Mr. Cheng has a slight smile on his face. Mr. Cheng never smiles.

Then, even more shocking, he replies by saying, "Thank you, Mr. Smythe. I wonder whether you and Mr. Brocktone would be good enough to run this meeting? Now that I have climbed the ladder of success to the very top, it is certainly time for me to stop kicking at the people climbing up from below me. It is time for me to not only get out of the way but also to help the rest of you climb up and become successful too. And I mean successful in a way that is for the highest good!"

"Thank you, Mr. Cheng," says Mr. Brocktone. "Mr. Smythe and I would like to introduce you all to the two newest members of our board: Pastor Larah Jones from the World Religious Summit and Aadhya Amin, the lead curator of the gardens at Raj Ghat. It is about time that the most powerful body in the world include some female bodies!"

"Amen!" whispers Pastor Jones.

Jakarta, Indonesia
Date: July 24, 2050

Mr. Kusumo from Indonesia, and the current president of the Group of Thirteen, convenes a special session of the leaders of the 13 biggest economic powers in the world.

"I want to welcome you to Indonesia for this special session. I am so glad you all could come. Special thanks to President Emily Browning from the United States, who was willing to fly here directly from New Delhi this morning. We also welcome Party Minister Yin from China and US Secretary of Peace Dr. Tasha Reeves, who we also invited to visit with us.

"We are meeting to start our first dialogue as a body of political leaders. I have projected a list of the SkyWoman's dialogue ground rules up on the east wall."

President Browning lifts a stick up above the table where she sits. "I have brought a talking stick, given to me by the great-grandmother Aaradhya Sargretti. Who would like to start speaking?"

President Çelik from Turkey takes the stick from President Browning's hand.

"Yes, well I have something to say. The people of Turkey are concerned that—"

"President Çelik, please note that one of our guidelines says that we always speak for ourselves, not for others," interrupts Mr. Kusumo.

"Very well then. I am still concerned that my country will disappear as the SkyWoman takes control of the world."

"Thank you for telling us what you are afraid of, President Çelik," Prime Minister Saanvi Anand responds. "I too noticed the same kind of fear inside me. I did a self-reflection and asked myself if it is possible that I am suffering from an Ego identification with my position and my nationality, like the SkyWoman has talked about."

"And what was the answer?"

"I discovered that, yes, I am identified both with being prime minister and with being an Indian. The SkyWoman showed me that I do not have to be ashamed that I have these identifications; they are common and natural. But they are also potentially dangerous because such identifications are actually a root cause of war and other forms of violence. This is because we humans become willing to attack and even kill others who seem to threaten what we identify with. I find that I can still love my job and my country without being identified with my role and nationality. I thus become free to love myself and other people."

Party Minister Yin from China stands to speak.

"I too have had a change of heart and mind. What the SkyWoman calls transformation. I wanted to come to the meeting to tell you all that I have a vision for what role politicians can play in a new world of transformational relationships.

"I would like to show you the vision through the kind of psychedrama that the SkyWoman has taught us. She will be helping me do this from her tent in New Delhi. We will look at how a politician might think and act when she is conscious of Ego."

Then Dr. Tasha Reeves, Secretary of Peace, stands to speak.

"And I am happy to be here as well. I will be entering in dialogue with other world leaders in the weeks to come and sharing what I have learned about how to set up and operate a Department of Peace in our government. Hopefully, we will join together to wage a world effort for deep peace in the years to come."

Rome, Italy
Date: July 24, 2050

Billy Lee climbs out of the Vatican hovercraft next to the Apostolic Palace. Three guards escort him inside and down a hall into the pope's study.

Pope Luca stands up to greet Billy Lee as he walks in. Billy Lee is surprised as the pope kisses him on his cheeks and invites him to sit. Their last interaction at the World Religious Summit was not quite as friendly.

"Billy Lee, thank you for coming to Rome to visit with me. I need your help. But first, I need to apologize. I was wrong to have you removed and silenced at the World Religious Summit.

"I have been praying about this every day, and God has shown me that the SkyWoman was also right. I am, as she would say, identified with my position of power in the church and in the World Religious Summit. I am not sure why it took me until I was sixty-seven to see the truth, but at least I saw it before I died.

"Yes, I am dying. The doctors cannot find a way to reverse the tumors that are growing in my body. Even the so-called immortality treatments cannot reverse the terminal illness I have. Despite all of this, I am no longer afraid of death, and I am ready to die.

"As the SkyWoman taught us, death is letting go of what is not me. I have let go of my identification with my position as pope. That does not mean that I have quit my job. It does mean I can do my job better because I no longer need to defend myself from the worship and hatred that any leader has to deal with.

"Idealization and demonization. That is pretty much all I experience from other people. Leaders are either worshiped as some kind of perfect being or hated for being full of nothing but imperfections. In either case, leaders are not seen accurately by others. It is all projection from the Ego of other people: what they hate in themselves, they hate in me; what they wish they were, they see in me.

"I am telling you all this, Billy, because there is a provision in the bylaws of the World Religious Summit, that allows the summit leader to appoint another in his or her place if the leader is no longer able to function. I am appointing you, Billy Lee, as the Leader of the Summit. I want you to facilitate a new kind of global organization where religious leaders engage in meditation and dialogue together to model the kind of transformational relationships that this world needs. Will you accept? Please?"

Astonished and humbled, Billy Lee can only nod his head silently in agreement. Then he leans forward and takes the pope's hand.

"Thank you. Your holiness."

"Please, just call me Luca. Or father."

"Yes, Father Luca. I want to suggest that we reach out to all the faith communities of the world as soon as possible. Transformative relationship building is a lifelong discipline, and the word discipline in your language means 'follower.' Since people often need a model to follow, I want to highlight the work of two of my friends from the Circle of 21: Imam Hussein and Rabbi Galante, both from Jerusalem. They have something to teach us all because they have learned how to disidentify from their beliefs enough to bridge the hatred between their faith communities and form a transformative friendship. Perhaps they can tell their story at the beginning of our Eternity Dialogues."

"Good idea, my son. Thank you."

Incheon National University, Korea
Date: July 24, 2050

Dr. Jiu Kang and Dr. Adele Dubois sit together in the Faculty Hall at Incheon National University. This location was selected so that the 40 or so attendees could sit in a large circle in their chairs on the large, flat, and open floor.

Dr. Dubois stands up and smiles. "Welcome to our gathering, everyone, including those of you in the room here as well as those who are joining us through the Mental Web. It was kind of you all to come here to Korea on such short notice. In future years, we hope to attract many more of the world's leading scientists and to give you much more time to make travel arrangements. As you all understand, we needed to meet quickly this year."

Dr. Kang stands up next to Dr. Dubois and hugs her.

"Yes, welcome to my country and university. We have called you here because each one of you is a leading scientist. As we all know, science has been increasingly under attack since the beginning of this century and millennium. Many of the world's leaders attack us simply because what we have discovered threatens their power, their wealth, and their privilege. Nevertheless, we have continued to seek the truth. Science is not always right. We have often made mistakes, but, ideally, we continue to seek the truth.

"We have shown, for example, how much of our current global climate change is caused by human activity, and we now know how to reverse the destruction we have inflicted upon global ecosystems.

"We are not the enemy of religions, nations, or corporations. We are the friend of truth."

There is applause in the room.

Dr. Dubois reenters the conversation. "Now we meet to take responsibility for our part in the Eternity Dialogues project that the SkyWoman has brought to us. Dr. Kang and I would like to propose that we create a federation of scientists who commit to the practice of meditation and dialogue for the purpose of individual and global transformation. Scientists need to model to other people that we can be both spiritually developed and intellectually developed. We humans are all ecobiopsychosocialspiritual beings.

"We have brought a friend of ours from the Circle of 21, Phil Parker of Salt Lake City, who has practiced Buddhism all of his life. He will be leading us in a meditation exercise, and then Dr. Kang and I will lead us in our first dialogue.

"We will also be proposing that all scientists study meditation and dialogue as part of their undergraduate studies. Universities also need to be grounded in both science and spirituality, and we must help our students develop in their awareness of ecology, emotional well-being, and transformational relationships."

Hainan, China
Date: July 24, 2050

Two men walk together into the village in Hainan, China.

In some ways, they are very different. Fifty-five years old now, General Pomsky has worked his way up to the highest levels of the Russian Army. He is feared by his peers and by his soldiers. Still a young man, Jean-Paul Martinez was recently the coleader of Global One, the most feared group of revolutionaries in the world. He was not so much feared as he was admired by his peers. That is until his best friend and "brother" Dmytro from the Ukraine was killed in a firefight with the police.

In some ways, they are both the same. Both men are warriors. Both are natural leaders. Both are courageous and willing to die if necessary. And both have had recent transformations.

They have arranged to meet with some of the remaining leaders of the Global One organization. The small house they are walking toward is in the village about 25 km from the center of the recent terrorist explosion on the island. Summoned by the SkyWoman, and promised by her that they would be safe, the operatives responsible for the delivery of the nuclear attack are all present. The Chinese people have not yet been made aware of the meeting.

When they enter the house, Jean-Paul knows two of the young men and greets them.

"Hello, it is good to see you, Bo and Nanda. We have not met for some time."

"Yes, these have been dangerous times for all of us. We are concerned that this is some kind of trap or trick, even though the SkyWoman has given her word for our safety."

"Understood," replies General Pomsky. "We have taken measures to ensure your safety and ours."

Then Jean-Paul recognizes Alex, the man who replaced him in the organization.

"Alex, how are you?"

"I'm scared out of my pants, quite frankly. We were all summoned mentally by the SkyWoman and asked to show up here. We've been fearing for our lives all morning."

"Yes, and General Pomsky and I are as committed to your safety as you are. Dialogue cannot happen in an atmosphere where physical safety is threatened because violence is a monologue that silences the Other. If we wanted to harm you, we would have already done that."

"So what do you want from us?"

"I want to kill you," responds General Pomsky, "but only in a sense. I want to kill the part of all of you that operates out of fear and shame and Ego. We cannot afford anymore to hate each other because we will all die, and everything that matters to us will die with us."

Smiling inside, Jean-Paul watches his old companions as they react to General Pomsky's unapologetic directness.

"How do we bridge the differences that divide us?" asks Jean-Paul. "Well, we will start today by sharing breakfast and our stories. I understand that our hosts have prepared stuffed buns, fried rice, and pork. We have time, and we have nowhere else to go.

"There is always a middle ground, a radical middle. Everyone in the room is a warrior. Each of us has a story to tell about how we became warriors and what we have seen and think we have learned. You know, my brothers, a story is sometimes the shortest distance between two people and between two perspectives."

General Pomsky starts. "Gentlemen, I am twice your age, but I still remember being like you. I remember being twenty-five and commanding one of my first missions. After the Americans left Afghanistan, there was much turmoil, the fighting was destabilizing the region, and we had to step in.

"I led thirty of my best Spetsnaz soldiers on a mission to take out the headquarters of one of the warring bands. Intelligence indicated that they were located in a system of hillside caves northeast of Kabul and that the site was vulnerable. We came in at night in hovercrafts.

"Well, the intelligence was compromised, and we were ambushed. Only five of us returned alive."

He rolls up his sleeve, revealing a muscular arm, some tattoos, and a long scar.

"I took a mortar fragment that fractured my radius. It still aches from time to time, usually in the winter. Vodka helps. But all the Vodka in Russia can never take away the memory of my soldiers dying all around me or that feeling of helpless rage and my guilt."

The room is quiet. Alex stands up. He is a tall thin white man with intense, sad eyes.

"I have memories that haunt me too. My family immigrated to Sweden from Poland about a year before England had their first Brexit vote to leave the European Union. There had been growing resentment in many Western countries toward immigrants from Eastern Europe. That was what a lot of the Brexit business was about in England, just the typical fear people have regarding anyone who looks or acts different than them. It was the same in Sweden.

"Well, someone set off a bomb in a Catholic Church that a number of Poles attended in Gothenburg. The police never seemed to be able to identify, much less find, the murderers, and when my sister and I participated in one of the protest marches we staged, someone threw a rock at the police and an officer fired live ammunition on us. I watched my sister die in my arms."

The dialogue continues into the evening. Many stories are shared, and the men sitting in the cheap furniture in the little house get to know each other better.

General Pomsky stands up. "Gentlemen, it is time for us to leave. It has been a privilege. In my country, we tell stories about the great ancient Russian warriors who we know as the Bogatyrs. The Bogatyrs did not seek glory so much as they attempted to be good people. Although I do not agree with all of your beliefs and behaviors, I see you as like the Bogatyrs. You are also good people who have tried to do good in the world."

The room is full of handshakes and then hugs as the visitors leave.

Location: Loiyangalani on Lake Turkana, Great Rift Valley, Kenya
Date: July 24, 2050

The Great-Grandmothers sit in a circle as they always have. It is early evening, and the stars are reappearing. Dark as the night, an older woman stands up.

"Welcome to all of you and to our two guests. I am Barannda Estava Maronna, great-granddaughter of Misorri Estava Maronna. It has been a long time since we invited guests to the circle. We have been a little busy lately, have we not, saving Earth?"

She laughs softly and the other women all laugh with her.

"And it is so good again to share another beautiful African evening with all of you under the Sky's Spine!"

They all look up to see what Westerners call the Milky Way, the great collection of maybe 250 billion stars in the galaxy that Earth's solar system rotates through. It seems to burn brighter than ever tonight.

"I have asked my sister Aaradhya Sargretti to bring our guests here to Africa. Aaradhya, would you please introduce them?"

"Yes, my sister. To my left is Yu Yan Zhou from Hainan, China. To my right is Nasteeho Sagal from Somalia."

Barannda stands up slowly, walks over first to Yu Yan Zhou, and sits down in front of her, taking her hand.

"My dear Yu Yan. We have been watching you, and we can see the love you have for the earth and for all the people on the planet. We want to invite you to join the Great-Grandmothers."

Yu Yan is crying softly. "Thank you, Mother-of-Us-All. I am honored. Aaradhya has talked to me about what is expected, and I accept the responsibilities I will be taking on."

Then Barannda slowly moves to sit in front of Nasteeho Sagal, taking her hand as well.

"Dear child, all of us have fallen in love with you. We have felt the energy of your wisdom and your love, which stands out among all the people on our continent. You have developed your spirituality far beyond what we usually see in people your age. Over the thousands of years that the Great-Grandmothers have taken care of our Earth, we have occasionally invited a young woman like yourself to join us at an early age, much like a spiritual intern. We will expect from you the same rigorous spiritual commitment that we do of all the Great-Grandmothers."

Nasteeho smiles her great gorgeous smile. "Thank you so much." Then her face changes, and she grows serious. "I am uncertain, Mother-of-Us-All. I want to join the Great-Grandmothers and be of service to all people. But my biological mother, my brothers, and my sisters also need me at home. I know I have so much to learn; there is so much wisdom to gain in life."

Barannda smiles a Nasteeho. "Your response comes from your loving heart and your growing wisdom. We do not ask that you leave your family that needs you. In time, you may also decide to have your own children, like I did many years ago. With your many gifts, you may decide to become a leader and healer in your village or in your country, like I also did from time to time. Please take your time to decide what you want to do. There is no rush. You have all of eternity to decide."

CHAPTER 33

Sky's Spine

Key themes in scene:
1. Membership in such things as religion, nationality,
ethnicity, and culture can offer people a sense of belonging
and security. However, Ego identification with such things
can also lead to violence and destruction
2. The people of Earth ultimately are capable of
dealing effectively with their own challenges

If one could watch the earth through the eyes of the SkyWoman, one would see everything within sight connected together by lines of energy, slowing rotating within the Sky's Spine, or Milky Way, as our galaxy wanders through the universe. Within this enormous galaxy, which looks like a luminous rotating spider's web, all living things participate in playing their own parts in this giant orchestra of energy and light. Human beings, conscious of their own consciousness, go about their daily routines mostly still unaware of their connections with everything, mostly feeling alone and lonely.

Location: Raj Ghat, New Delhi, India
Date: July 25, 2050

The SkyWoman sits in front of the Circle of 21 and the Great-Grandmothers. Yu Yan Zhou and Nasteeho Sagal now sit on the floor with the Great-Grandmothers.

"Hello, people of Earth. We sit together one more time with the Circle of 21 and the Great-Grandmothers. We are meeting to do one more meditation together. We have done a great deal of work in a short time. There is much more to do. There is no rush since we have all of eternity.

"As we have discussed, the highest state of joy available to humans is the ecstatic state in which, as some of your ancestors said, 'I stand beside myself' in joy and love.

The ecstatic state is not a state of denial in which I actually forget about myself or the world. Instead, it is a state of consciousness available to all of us in which I stand beside myself in reverent awareness, seeing myself and the universe accurately and lovingly.

"I want to share this idea with you before I leave, because ecstasy is the fuel for human love. All of your major wisdom traditions have taught what you call the golden rule, to love others as you love yourself. But over all these years, humanity has not yet learned to express the loving-kindness that you are capable of expressing toward each other. Why is this?

"You actually have learned to practice the golden rule very effectively. Most people do treat others exactly the way they treat themselves. Unfortunately, you mostly hate yourselves, so you naturally project your hatred onto others.

"Yes, the challenge with your golden rule, my children, is that you do not actually love yourselves. How can I express loving-kindness when I hate myself? Don't take my word for it. Look inside and see if it is true.

"And do not confuse narcissism with self-love anymore. Narcissism is an Ego-driven attempt to be superior to others in compensation for the self-hatred, or shame, that every one of you harbors inside. The Ego compares and drives humans to assess their worth relative to everyone else.

"My fellow travelers, when you feel either superior or inferior to other people, other living things, or the universe itself, it is your Ego that is driving your thinking and feeling. Thus feelings of superiority and feelings of inferiority are two sides of the same Ego coin.

"Is there a medicine for this self-hatred? Once again, the medicine is your own consciousness, which is a more friendly way to view all that is. Long ago, when I started to see my own self-hatred, I saw how it was related to my Ego disconnection with myself and the universe, and my disconnection with eternity and infinity. At first, I hated my own self-hatred, which, of course, was the Ego's way of staying in power, for the Ego feeds on hatred of any kind. I began to heal when I instead started to apply consciousness, reverent awareness, to my self-hatred. In a real sense, I learned to love my self-hatred. I held my self-hatred in my arms, so to speak, like I would hold a precious baby in my arms. As we have discussed, I cannot kill my Ego, but I can change my relationship with my Ego. Similarly, I cannot kill my self-hatred, but I change my relationship with my self-hatred. And when I am conscious of my hatred, as when I am conscious of Ego, hatred loses its power in that moment.

"Since I cannot kill the Ego, consciousness is a practice for my whole life, for eternity. Eternity and infinity live together, my children, in every moment we are alive in this incredible universe. One way to enter the spiritual perspective is to see infinity and eternity in the moment. When I do this, I see my own life challenges in a new much larger perspective. I will show you."

As all the people of Earth watch, the Sky Woman first shows everyone a luminous view of his or her individual body. Each person sees his or her body as a glowing system of energy connected within and without.

"Let us travel first into the smaller dimensions that will take us to an experience of infinity and eternity within."

The people are now able to see inside their own bodies. They see oxygen entering the lungs, the blood flowing through the lungs and moving the oxygen to the cells of the brain, and the electrical currents moving through the nervous system. Then the view goes smaller. Individual oxygen atoms become visible. The people can see inside one particular oxygen atom. They travel through the mostly empty space of that oxygen atom and travel through the wave orbits of the eight electrons. They see the eight neutrons and eight protons in the nucleus. Then they enter the nucleus and see how each of the neutrons and protons is made up of quarks held together by gluons. Then the people are given a peek into the underlying structures of the quarks and gluons, structures that scientists have still not yet discovered. There is a sense that there are even other things yet smaller and smaller, perhaps going on into an infinity of smallness.

The people go back to a view of their bodies again.

"Let us travel now into the larger dimensions where an experience of infinity and eternity also exists."

The people watch as the view of the human body expands to a view of the earth and then the solar system in which the earth now belongs, along with the other planets and many other rotating objects that circle the sun. Then the view shifts to the Milky Way, and the people can see the many solar systems and other objects rotating in a great spiral around the immense "black hole" at the galaxy's very center.

The people next can see the local group of galaxies within which their own "Sky's Spine" Galaxy, the Andromeda Galaxy, and over 50 smaller dwarf galaxies rotate in an enormous path through space-time.

The view enlarges again. The people see the Laniakea Supercluster of galaxies, which is the home of their own local group and approximately 100,000 other nearby galaxies. The size of Earth is dwarfed incomprehensively again as the point of reference enlarges.

Then everyone can see how the universe is made up of a web-like network of filaments, including galaxy walls, supercluster complexes, and galaxy sheets. These are the largest structures that Earth's scientists have detected. The biggest ones are about 260 million light-years across, full of galaxy superclusters. The view is awesome and beautiful. Between these filaments is darkness, apparent empty space.

The Sky Woman next reveals a hint of even larger structures, still undetected by humans, perhaps even beyond what humans call the "universe."

Then the view suddenly collapses as the space-time perspective shifts, and everything in the universe shrinks to a tiny point, smaller than any known structure. This is the beginning of what humans now call the universe and perhaps the ending, an infinitely small point consisting of an infinitely large amount of energy mass.

"So, my fellow travelers, if we seek the larger perspective, we also find the tiniest of structures. As we get bigger, we eventually get smaller, and when we get smaller, we eventually get bigger. That is what some of your scientists and theoreticians suspected when they invented their theory of the 'big bang' as the start of the observable current universe.

"What you call 'time' also moves in a great circle. All time actually exists right now as well. I offer these visions to all of you as meditation themes you can use in your lives to come, especially when you feel discouraged and Ego has returned to try to take back control.

"Remember that it is the mysteries of Creation that can often inform our lives much more than the 'facts' we currently think we know."

The SkyWoman pauses.

"And now it is time for me to leave you. In preparation, I still have a few more things to say. Much of what I have to say may be difficult for you to hear, but I have to talk with you about these things before I go. I do not want you to take my words as necessarily true, but I challenge you to find out for yourselves if they are true. You can only find the truth if you are willing to see your own conditioning and let go of the assumptions you have been conditioned to believe. In a sense, I cannot tell you anything that you all don't already know on some level. The truth is always available for all humans to see.

"First, most of the people of Earth now consider yourselves to be religious. Your word religion was a beautiful word that meant in Latin 'to bring together.' Religion has brought humans together, but it also has separated you from each other and from the universe.

"In ancient times, humans shared their particular religions with others in their families and tribes. The religion bonded the people of the tribe together and gave them common beliefs and rituals. Then people became identified with these beliefs and rituals, and tended to devalue and dehumanize other tribes who thought and acted differently. Thus religion made intertribal violence possible. To have deep peace on Earth, religious people will need to transform the way they see themselves and others by thinking bigger and by seeing the people of Earth as one tribe on a small beautiful planet in an immense universe. Thinking from a different perspective can inform our spiritual viewpoint.

"Thus, instead of just bringing the tribe together through religion or through any other means, the people of Earth can think about bringing together all the people of the earth. People do not have to give up their religion, and they do not need to share the same beliefs and rituals to do this, but they do need to become conscious of their identifications with the beliefs and rituals they share with their own local 'tribes.'

"Most of the people of Earth also identify with your national, cultural, and ethnic identities. Much like religion, these kinds of identities also served humanity when most lived in tribes. When people identified with their tribal and cultural and ethnic identities, they worked hard to protect and assist each other. Today, of course, most of you live in nations, and that same desire to protect 'your own people' still exists. Unfortunately, when there is an 'in-group,' there is always also an 'outgroup.' When you identify with your nation, culture, or ethnicity, there is that Ego tendency to devalue and dehumanize the Other. And violence and war become possible. As we have discussed, the medicine for Egoitis is consciousness. As you see for yourselves whether what I say is true, you can transform Ego.

"In fact, my children, any kind of identity formation is ultimately a source of violence. This is because every one of you is much more than any identity you may give yourself or be given by others. I cannot identify with a religion or nationality, for example, without excluding those who identify differently than me; and that exclusion is a form of violence. The violence is directed first toward you, because when you identify with something that is not you, you lose contact with your connection with the universe. Yes, your only true identity is your connection with the Great Mystery, with everything there is, with love.

"Thus when I identify with, for example, my family, wealth, power, skin color, political party, what church I might attend, what country I happen to live in, who I love, or the age I am, I am identifying ultimately with who I am not, and I am separating myself from other people who may look or talk or act differently.

"As we have discussed, when I am willing to let go of what is not me, when I am willing to die to that which is not me, I am able to have my true birthright, which is membership in the eternal and infinite universe. I do not have to stop loving my country, my faith, my family, or my culture. In fact, identification is not love at all but a process that comes out of fear. I want to dis-identify with these things that are not me, so I am free to be connected with and to love everything.

"Finally, I want to remind you that your identification with being human also divides you from other living things, as well as from the rest of the universe. Just like you cannot love yourself, your family, or your tribe and at the same time hate everyone else, you cannot love humans and at the same time devalue other living things or devalue the air, the water, and the stars. All life and all elements of Creation need to be cared for. After I have left you, the Great-Grandmothers will show you how to view the universe through the eyes of an owl, through the leaves of the tree, and through the energy of the sun, for example. The birds, the plants, and the other elements of the universe all have much to teach humanity. And you have your loving consciousness to offer them.

"Love is the answer, as many of your poets and teachers say, but it may not be what you think. Love is not bound by identities; it is always free, and expansive, and spiritually grounded, or it does not exist. What you call love is usually a reaction to your anxiety, fear, and shame. You say you love your partner, but perhaps you actually *cling to your partner more because you feel afraid of being alone and afraid you are not loveable. You think you love your children, but perhaps you are more afraid that you will die, and you want a legacy to carry on afterward. Similarly, you say you love your religion, your tribe, and your country, but perhaps you mostly want to belong to something larger because you do not really value yourself. Look at these things honestly with what we have called consciousness, and you will become free to love.*

"I have asked the Great-Grandmothers to be your teachers. They will hold sacred space for all of you to do the Eternity Dialogues in the years and millennia to come. They will bring the sacred feminine voice back to the world, which has been subservient to the sacred masculine for many years. They will be working first with the Circle of 21 to help them facilitate the dialogues that need to happen.

"I wish now to say good-bye to all of you. You do not need me to guide you anymore. I just came to remind you about who you are and who you are not. I could not save my own planet. I cannot by myself save Earth. But, my fellow travelers, you can.

"Do not be afraid of being alone, because that is part of being a human being, conscious of your own consciousness. You realize you are alive and that you someday die, and there is a certain aloneness to this, but such aloneness cannot harm you if you face it every day. It is loneliness, which is the fear of and the running from aloneness that causes you harm.

"I only know what I know, but I can tell you that I am not aware of any other race of intelligent beings in our galaxy. After the Sky Woman leaves, humanity may learn to finally face the responsibility of being alone in this beautiful galaxy and taking full response-ability for its own future.

"As for the rest of the universe? Who knows. It is part of the Great Mystery we are all blessed with.

"I have lived a long time and wish to rest awhile. From the land I was born in, I have looked up into the night sky all my life and wished to return to the center of our great home galaxy that many of you here in India call Akasaganga or in Europe the Milky Way, or in Africa Sky's Spine. Everything here on Earth, after all, came through our great parent galaxy. We are all children of the Sky's Spine."

The Sky Woman starts to glow in a brighter indigo color, and she lifts up slowly into the air. The Circle of 21 and the Great-Grandmothers watch as she rises in the warm Indian sky. Gathering speed, the indigo light shrinks in size and then disappears into the cumulus clouds.

There is a collective gasp as the people of Earth realize they are alone. But perhaps not lonely anymore.

Location: Loiyangalani on Lake Turkana, Great Rift Valley, Kenya
Date: July 25, 2050

Not long afterward, the Great-Grandmothers sit together again on the shore of Lake Turkana. It is dark, and a warm breeze is coming off the water. The sky is bright with stars. They wait quietly in a sacred circle.

They all look up to see the SkyWoman descending from the clear sky. Glowing in indigo light, she silently puts her feet on the earth one more time.

The indigo light brightens for an instant and then slowly disappears. A small, dark, very old woman stands in front of them, now only illuminated by the stars.

"Good evening," she says warmly. "I am Barannda Estava Maronna, great-granddaughter of Misorri Estava Maronna. Welcome to all of you again. It is good to sit with you once more on this sacred land."

Sitting next to her, Aaradhya Sargretti smiles. "Welcome back Mother-of-All-of-Us. And nice landing!"

The other great-grandmothers laugh.

Sitting in the circle, Nasteeho Sagal's mouth is wide open in astonishment.

"What? Wait ... Great-Grandmother, *you* are the SkyWoman? Or is the SkyWoman you?"

Yu Yan Zhou is equally surprised. "Did you disguise yourself, Great-Grandmother? And why?"

"And how did you learn to fly?" asks Nasteeho.

Barannda's teeth are lit by starlight as she smiles at Nasteeho.

"Well, my child, when you become as old as I am, you will have had enough time to learn a few tricks. You can learn to fly too, in time. Actually, there are many more important things that we can learn. But yes, flying *is* fun."

Barannda looks at Yu Yan and becomes more serious.

"And, yes, I am the SkyWoman. It was not a lie. Everything I told the people of Earth is true. I *am* a refugee from a planet that was destroying itself. That planet is, of course, Earth itself. And the Great-Grandmothers did ask me to come back to Earth as I did."

She pauses to look up at the sky.

"We started planning the SkyWoman's visit hundreds of years ago, my sisters. With the acceleration of technological progress, we could see the Great Convergence coming. We knew that the people of Earth would not listen to, much less believe, a group of old women, especially if we claimed to be as old as we really are. We knew that most of the people of Earth already believed that aliens will eventually come from outer space and will either destroy us or save us. We decided to reveal our wisdom to the people of Earth through the SkyWoman."

"But are there actually real-life aliens in the universe who will come to visit humanity?" asks Nasteeho. "My mother has talked about people from the village seeing UFOs in the sky."

Barannda smiles again. "What would you prefer to believe, child? That there are aliens from other planets and other galaxies or that humanity is the only race of beings in the universe who are conscious of our own consciousness?"

"Oh, I want there to be aliens who would come with their spaceships and advanced technology," Nasteeho responds quickly.

"Yes, my dear. And most of humanity feels the way you do."

Barannda glances for a moment at Aaradhya Sargretti, who has been sitting quietly across the circle from her. "And as the SkyWoman said, after all these years, we have never had contact with or sensed another intelligent extraterrestrial race. Humanity may very well be alone."

"And our aloneness may be our salvation. There may never be any space aliens, or goddesses, or gods who will come down to save us," adds Aaradhya. "So we must take responsibility ourselves for what we think and do, and not continue trying to escape into loneliness, which is itself just our fear of our aloneness!"

"Are you hopeful then?" asks Yu Yan Zhou. "Hopeful that humanity will transform itself? Will we learn how to love, cooperate to care for the earth, and, eventually, travel together through space?"

Aaradhya responds, "We do not talk of hope, because when we hope, we leave the present and long for a future that does not exist. Better to be conscious in this moment because now is the only time there is. And right now, on this planet, there are many who are working on developing their consciousness."

"Yes, and it is time now, my sisters." Barannda Estava Maronna points up at the Sky's Spine, brilliant and hazy in the night sky. "I wish to take rest in the sky with my ancestors."

"Will you return?" Nasteeho cries out.

"You are all my children. I will never leave you, so there is no need for me to return."

And with that, the Great-Grandmothers watch as Barannda starts to rise up again toward the center of the Sky's Spine, slowly at first and then at tremendous speed.

And the windless African sky is quiet.

Mauna Kea Observatory, Hawaii
Date: July 25, 2050

Because Mauna Kea has long been a sacred mountain of Hawaii's First Peoples, the observatories built there were always controversial. The new observatory, the most powerful in the world, was named Nō ala Wiliau Hōkū, which is Hawaiian for "Milky Way Galaxy."

Sitting at the control center that night is Dr. Zahara Keahi, lead astronomer at the observatory. It is an exceptionally dark and clear night, and Dr. Keahi decides to view the constellation of Sagittarius, where the apparent center of the Milky Way also happens to reside.

As she watches, she suddenly sees what appears to be a gigantic, brilliant star glowing as it flies across the central region of the great galaxy. It first leaves a trail of indigo light behind it, like a comet often leaves a glowing tail of illumination. Then that tail of light transforms into a brilliant rainbow of all the colors, arching across the great galactic center before it fades from view.

Pictures of the phenomenon soon appear in the TeleTouch news all over the world.

Names of Key People in the Novel

Members of the Circle of 21, Participants in the First Dialogue

Women

President Emily Browning, United States

Dr. Tasha Reeves, secretary of peace, United States

Deanna Bradley, Global Multinationals Unlimited

Pastor Larah Jones, World Religious Summit

Prime Minister Saanvi Anand, India

Dr. Jiu Kang, Incheon National University in Korea

Aaradhya Sargretti, Great-Grandmother

Aadhya Amin, the lead curator of the gardens at Raj Ghat

Nasteeho Sagal, Somalia

Dr. Adele Dubois, University of Lorraine in Nancy, France

Yu Yan Zhou, China

Men

Phil Parker, Salt Lake City

Jean-Paul Martinez, Global One

Party Minister Yin, China

Imam Hussein, Jerusalem

Rabbi Galante, Jerusalem

Billy Lee, World Religious Summit

Mr. Smythe, CEO GMU

Mr. Brocktone, CEO GMU

Mr. Kusumo, President of the Group of Thirteen, Indonesia

General Pomsky, Russian Army

Other Characters

Greater Bay Area Biotech (a Subsidiary of Biotech Industries International or Bi2)

Randy Snyder, clinic manager

Dr. Yin, clinic medical director

Dr. Delores Walker, staff psychiatrist

Mr. Hauser, the first immortality treatment patient in the United States

Global Multinationals Unlimited

Mr. Cheng, president

Group of Thirteen

Mr. Kusumo, president, Indonesia

Mr. Schmidt, Germany

President Çelik, Turkey

Premier Petrov, Russia

Chairman Lau, China

President Sousa, Brazil

2050 World Summit of Religious Leaders

Pope Luca, Summit Leader

Reverend Willy Mandly, leader of Apocalypticism Committee

Pastor Ravis, member of Social Action Committee (chaired by Pastor Larah Jones)

Global One

Dmytro, lieutenant, Ukraine (adopted "brother" of Jean-Paul, another lieutenant from Colombia)

Alex, lieutenant, Sweden (takes over Global One after Dmytro is killed)

Some of the Nine Billion People Who Participated in the First Global Meditations and Dialogues

Bo is the husband of Yu Yan Zhou. They live in Haikou, Hainan. Bo went to Haikou City People's Hospital after suffering a concussion in the nuclear explosion.

Duco Sagal is the mother of Nasteeho Sagal. They live near the beach in Hobyo (Obbia), Somalia.

Sid is the partner of Phil Parker. They live with their three children Matti, Benton, and Frederick in the suburbs of Salt Lake City, Utah.

Government of India

Seetha Devi, chief of staff for Prime Minister Anand

Great-Grandmothers

Barannda Estava Maronna, great-granddaughter of Misorri Estava Maronna, born near Lake Turkana, Great Rift Valley, Kenya, about 200,000 years ago, leader of the Great-Grandmothers.

Aaradhya Sargretti, great-Granddaughter of Kashvri Sargretti, born near what is now called New Delhi, India, about 50,000 years ago, second to Barannda in leadership of the Great-Grandmothers.

CPSIA information can be obtained
at www.ICGtesting.com
Printed in the USA
FSHW021652230819
61364FS